I2

Mathematical language

This publication forms part of an Open University course. Details of this and other Open University courses can be obtained from the Student Registration and Enquiry Service, The Open University, PO Box 197, Milton Keynes, MK7 6BJ, United Kingdom: tel. +44 (0)870 300 6090, e-mail general-enquiries@open.ac.uk

Alternatively, you may visit the Open University website at http://www.open.ac.uk where you can learn more about the wide range of courses and packs offered at all levels by The Open University.

To purchase a selection of Open University course materials, visit http://www.ouw.co.uk, or contact Open University Worldwide, Michael Young Building, Walton Hall, Milton Keynes, MK7 6AA, United Kingdom, for a brochure: tel. +44 (0)1908 858793, fax +44 (0)1908 858787, e-mail ouw-customer-services@open.ac.uk

The Open University, Walton Hall, Milton Keynes, MK7 6AA.

First published 2006. Reprinted with amendments 2007.

Copyright © 2006 The Open University

All rights reserved; no part of this publication may be reproduced, stored in a retrieval system, transmitted or utilised in any form or by any means, electronic, mechanical, photocopying, recording or otherwise, without written permission from the publisher or a licence from the Copyright Licensing Agency Ltd. Details of such licences (for reprographic reproduction) may be obtained from the Copyright Licensing Agency Ltd, Saffron House, 6–10 Kirby Street, London EC1N 8TS; website http://www.cla.co.uk.

Open University course materials may also be made available in electronic formats for use by students of the University. All rights, including copyright and related rights and database rights, in electronic course materials and their contents are owned by or licensed to The Open University, or otherwise used by The Open University as permitted by applicable law.

In using electronic course materials and their contents you agree that your use will be solely for the purposes of following an Open University course of study or otherwise as licensed by The Open University or its assigns.

Except as permitted above you undertake not to copy, store in any medium (including electronic storage or use in a website), distribute, transmit or re-transmit, broadcast, modify or show in public such electronic materials in whole or in part without the prior written consent of The Open University or in accordance with the Copyright, Designs and Patents Act 1988.

Edited, designed and typeset by The Open University, using the Open University TEX System.

Printed and bound in the United Kingdom by Hobbs the Printers Limited, Brunel Road, Totton, Hampshire SO40 3WX.

ISBN 0 7492 0205 X

1.2

Contents

Introduction

In our everyday lives we use language to develop ideas and to communicate them to other people. In this unit we examine ways in which language is adapted to express mathematical ideas.

When we try to use ordinary language to explore mathematics, the words involved may not have a precise meaning, or may have more than one meaning. Many words have meanings that evolve as people adapt their understanding of them to accord with new experiences and new ideas. At any given time, one person's interpretation of language may differ from another person's interpretation, and this can lead to misunderstandings and confusion.

In mathematics we try to avoid these difficulties by expressing our thoughts in terms of well-defined mathematical objects. These objects can be anything from numbers and geometrical shapes to more complicated objects, usually constructed from numbers, points and functions. We discuss these objects using precise language which should be interpreted in the same way by everyone. In this unit we introduce the basic mathematical language needed to express the range of mathematical concepts in this course.

In Section 1 we discuss the idea of a *set* and describe some ways to define sets. We illustrate our discussion with sets of numbers and with geometrical sets of points in the plane. We also explain how to check whether two given sets are equal and whether one set is a subset of another. Finally, we introduce the set operations of *union*, *intersection* and *difference*.

In Section 2 we give the general definition of a *function*, and illustrate how functions can be used to describe a variety of mathematical concepts, such as transformations of the plane. We discuss the idea of *composing* two functions, and the idea of forming the *inverse* of a function.

In Section 3 we examine the language used to express mathematical statements and proofs, and discuss various techniques for proving that a mathematical statement is true. These techniques include *direct proof*, *proof by mathematical induction*, *proof by contradiction* and *proof by contraposition*. We also illustrate the use of *counter-examples* to show that a statement is false.

Section 4 introduces some important theorems used later in the course.

Study guide

Sections 1 and 2 contain basic material that will be used throughout the course. It is vital that you familiarise yourself with the ideas and notation introduced in these two sections.

The material in Section 3 should help you to follow the proofs that you will meet later in the course, and to communicate mathematics effectively yourself. You may find that you work though this section rather more slowly than the others. You may prefer to study it in two sessions, with Subsections 3.1 to 3.4 in the first and Subsections 3.5 to 3.8 in the second.

Section 4 has some basic identities needed in Unit I3 and Analysis Block A.

1   Sets

After working through this section, you should be able to:

(a) use set notation;

(b) determine whether two given sets are equal and whether one given set is a subset of another;

(c) find the *union, intersection* and *difference* of two given sets.

1.1 What is a set?

In mathematics we frequently consider collections of objects of various kinds. We may, for example, consider:

- the solutions of a quadratic equation;
- the points on a circle;
- the prime numbers less than 100;
- the vertices of a triangle;
- the domain of a real function.

A *prime number* is an integer n, greater than 1, whose only positive factors are 1 and n; the first few primes are 2, 3, 5, 7, 11, 13, 17.

The concept of a *set* provides the unifying framework needed to investigate such collections systematically.

You can think of a **set** as a collection of objects, such as numbers, points, functions, or even other sets. Each object in a set is an **element** or **member** of the set, and the elements **belong to** the set, or are **in** the set.

There is no limitation on the types of object that may appear in a set, provided that the set is specified in a way that enables us to decide, in principle, whether a given object is in the set.

There are many ways of making such a specification. For example, we can define S to be the set of numbers in the list

4, 9, 3, 2.

This enables us to decide that the number 2 (say) is in S, but that the number 1 (say) is not in S. We can illustrate this set by a diagram, as shown in the margin; such a diagram is called a **Venn diagram**, after the 19th-century Cambridge mathematician John Venn.

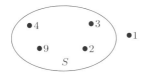

We can also define a set E by stating

let E be the set of all even integers.

The symbol S is a label for the set, *not* a member of the set. Similar labels will appear in other diagrams.

This description enables us to determine whether a given object is in E by deciding whether it is an even integer; for example, 6 is in E, but 5 is not.

Some sets are used so often that special symbols are reserved for them.

$\mathbb{R}$ denotes the set of real numbers.

$\mathbb{R}^*$ denotes the set of non-zero real numbers.

$\mathbb{Q}$ denotes the set of rational numbers.

$\mathbb{Z}$ denotes the set of integers $\ldots, -2, -1, 0, 1, 2, \ldots$.

$\mathbb{N}$ denotes the set of natural numbers $1, 2, 3, \ldots$.

A real number is a number with a decimal expansion (possibly infinite), for example, $\pi = 3.14\ldots$ or 1.1.

A rational number is a real number that can be expressed as a fraction, for example, $14/5$ or $-3/4$.

We use the symbol $\in$ to indicate membership of a set; for example, we indicate that 7 is a member of $\mathbb{N}$ by writing

$7 \in \mathbb{N}$.

We read this as '7 belongs to $\mathbb{N}$' or '7 is in $\mathbb{N}$'.

We indicate that -9 is *not* a member of $\mathbb{N}$ by writing

$-9 \notin \mathbb{N}$.

We read this as '-9 does not belong to $\mathbb{N}$' or '-9 is not in $\mathbb{N}$'.

We also use the symbol $\in$ when we wish to introduce a symbol that stands for an arbitrary element of a set. For example, we write

let $x \in \mathbb{R}$

to indicate that x is an arbitrary (unspecified) member of the set $\mathbb{R}$. We sometimes refer to x as a *real variable*. In general, a variable is a symbol (like x or n) that stands for an arbitrary element of a set.

Exercise 1.1   Which of the following statements are true?

(a) $-2 \in \mathbb{Z}$ (b) $5 \notin \mathbb{N}$ (c) $1.3 \notin \mathbb{Q}$

(d) $\frac{1}{2} \in \mathbb{N}$ (e) $-\pi \in \mathbb{R}$ (f) $2 \in \mathbb{Q}$

1.2 Set notation

We now examine some formal ways of specifying a set.

We can specify a set with a small number of elements by listing these elements between a pair of braces (curly brackets). For example, we can specify the set A consisting of the first five natural numbers by

$A = \{1, 2, 3, 4, 5\}$.

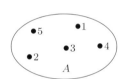

The membership of a set is not affected by the order in which its elements are listed, so we can specify this set A equally well by

$A = \{5, 2, 1, 4, 3\}$.

Similarly, we can specify the set B of vertices of the square shown in the margin by

$B = \{(0,0), (1,0), (1,1), (0,1)\}$.

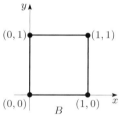

We can even specify a set C whose elements are the three sets $\{1, 3, 5\}$, $\{9, 4\}$ and $\{2\}$ by

$C = \{\{1, 3, 5\}, \{9, 4\}, \{2\}\}$.

A set with only one element, such as the set $\{2\}$, is called a **singleton**. (Do not confuse the *set* $\{2\}$ with the *number* 2.)

Exercise 1.2   Which of the following statements are true?

(a) $1 \in \{4, 3, 1, 7\}$

(b) $\{-9\} \in \{\{6, 1, 2\}, \{8, 7, 9, 5\}, \{-9\}, \{5, 4\}\}$

(c) $\{9\} \in \{5, 6, 7, 8, 9\}$

(d) $(0, 1) \in \{(1, 0), (1, 4), (2, 4)\}$

(e) $\{0, 1\} \in \{\{0, 1\}, \{1, 4\}, \{2, 4\}\}$

It does not matter if we specify a set element more than once within set brackets; we still describe the set that contains each specified element. For example,

$$\{1, 2, 3, 3\} \quad \text{and} \quad \{1, 2, 3\}$$

describe the same set. However, we usually try to avoid specifying an element more than once.

For a set with a large number of elements, it is not practicable to list all the elements, so we sometimes use three dots (called an *ellipsis*) to indicate that a particular pattern of membership continues. For example, we can specify the set consisting of the first 100 natural numbers by writing

$$\{1, 2, 3, \ldots, 100\}.$$

The use of an ellipsis can be extended to certain infinite sets. For example, we can specify the set of all natural numbers by writing

$$\{1, 2, 3, \ldots\}.$$

One disadvantage of this notation is that the pattern indicated by the ellipsis may be ambiguous. For example, it is not clear whether

$$\{3, 5, 7, \ldots\}$$

denotes the set of odd prime numbers or the set of odd natural numbers greater than 1. For this reason, this notation can be used only when the pattern of membership is obvious, or where an additional clarifying explanation is given.

An alternative way of specifying a set is to use variables to build up objects of the required type, and then write down the condition(s) that the variables must satisfy. For example, consider the open interval $(3, \infty)$, consisting of all real numbers x such that $x > 3$. Using set notation, we write this as

$$\{x \in \mathbb{R} : x > 3\},$$

which is read as follows:

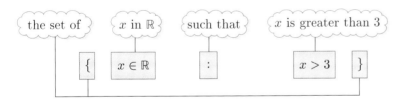

A set can often be described in several different ways using such set notation. In particular, we can use a letter other than x to denote an arbitrary (general) element of a set; for example, the above interval can also be written as

$$\{r \in \mathbb{R} : r > 3\}.$$

If it is necessary to include more than one condition after the colon, then we write either a comma or the word 'and' between the conditions. So the interval $(0, 1]$ can be written as

$$\{x \in \mathbb{R} : x > 0, \ x \leq 1\} \quad \text{or} \quad \{x \in \mathbb{R} : x > 0 \text{ and } x \leq 1\},$$

although usually we combine the inequalities and write

$$\{x \in \mathbb{R} : 0 < x \leq 1\}.$$

Sometimes it is convenient to specify a set by writing an expression in one or more variables before the colon, and the conditions on the variables after the colon. For example, the set of even integers less than 100 may be specified by

$$\{2k : k \in \mathbb{Z} \text{ and } k < 50\}.$$

Just as when we list the elements of a set, when we use set notation it does not matter if a set element is specified more than once. For example,

$$\{\sin x : x \in \mathbb{R}\} \quad \text{and} \quad \{x \in \mathbb{R} : -1 \le x \le 1\}$$

specify the same set.

Set notation is useful when we wish to refer to the set of solutions, called the **solution set**, of one or more equations. For example, the solutions of $x^2 = 1$ form the set

$$\{x \in \mathbb{R} : x^2 = 1\} = \{-1, 1\}.$$

The solution set of an equation depends on the set of values from which the solutions are taken. For example, the solution set of the equation

$$(x - 1)(2x - 1) = 0$$

is

$$\{x \in \mathbb{R} : (x - 1)(2x - 1) = 0\} = \{1, \tfrac{1}{2}\}$$

if we are interested in real solutions, but is

$$\{x \in \mathbb{Z} : (x - 1)(2x - 1) = 0\} = \{1\}$$

if we are interested only in integer solutions. In this unit we assume that solutions are taken from $\mathbb{R}$ unless otherwise stated.

Sometimes an equation has *no* real solutions, so its solution set has no elements. This set is called the **empty set** and is denoted by $\varnothing$. For example,

$$\{x \in \mathbb{R} : x^2 = -1\} = \varnothing.$$

Example 1.1   Use set notation to specify each of the following:

(a) the set of all natural numbers greater than 50;

(b) the set of all real solutions of the equation $x^4 + 8x^2 + 16 = 0$;

(c) the set of all odd integers.

Solution

(a) The elements of this set are the natural numbers n such that $n > 50$. So the set is

$$\{n \in \mathbb{N} : n > 50\}.$$

(b) The elements of this set are the real numbers x that satisfy the given equation. So the set is

$$\{x \in \mathbb{R} : x^4 + 8x^2 + 16 = 0\}.$$

In fact, the given equation has no real solutions, so this set is the empty set $\varnothing$.

(c) An odd integer is one that can be written in the form $2k + 1$, for some integer k. So the set is

$$\{2k + 1 : k \in \mathbb{Z}\}. \quad \blacksquare$$

Exercise 1.3   Use set notation to specify each of the following:

(a) the set of integers greater than -2 and less than 1000;

(b) the closed interval $[2, 7]$;

(c) the set of positive rational numbers with square greater than 2;

(d) the set of even natural numbers;

(e) the set of integer powers of 2.

1.3 Plane sets

In Unit I1 you met the plane $\mathbb{R}^2$, and saw that each point in the plane can be represented as an ordered pair (x, y) with respect to a given pair of axes. A set of points in $\mathbb{R}^2$ is called a **plane set** or a **plane figure**. Simple examples of plane sets are lines and circles.

Such plane sets occur in many applications of mathematics; for example, in computer graphics.

Lines

Consider a straight line l with slope a and y-intercept b. This line is the set of all points (x, y) in the plane such that $y = ax + b$. Using set notation, we write this as

$$l = \{(x, y) \in \mathbb{R}^2 : y = ax + b\}.$$

(We sometimes refer to 'the line $y = ax + b$' as a shorthand way of specifying this set.)

For a line parallel to the y-axis with x-intercept c, we write

$$l = \{(x, y) \in \mathbb{R}^2 : x = c\}.$$

Exercise 1.4

(a) Use set notation to specify the line l with slope 2 that passes through the point $(0, 5)$.

(b) Sketch the line $l = \{(x, y) \in \mathbb{R}^2 : y = 1 - x\}$.

Circles

The **unit circle** U is the set of points (x, y) in the plane whose distance from the origin $(0, 0)$ is 1. By Pythagoras' Theorem, these are the points (x, y) for which $x^2 + y^2 = 1$, so, in set notation, the unit circle is written as

$$U = \{(x, y) \in \mathbb{R}^2 : x^2 + y^2 = 1\}.$$

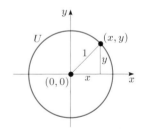

In general, the circle C of radius r centred at the point (a, b) is the set of points (x, y) that lie at a distance r from (a, b). By Pythagoras' Theorem, these are the points (x, y) satisfying the equation $(x - a)^2 + (y - b)^2 = r^2$, so, in set notation, this circle is written as

$$C = \{(x, y) \in \mathbb{R}^2 : (x - a)^2 + (y - b)^2 = r^2\}.$$

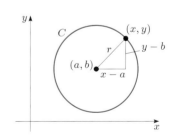

Exercise 1.5

(a) Use set notation to specify the circle C of radius 3 centred at $(1, -4)$.

(b) Sketch the circle $C = \{(x, y) \in \mathbb{R}^2 : (x - 1)^2 + (y - 3)^2 = 4\}$.

Half-planes, discs and other plane sets

Consider the line

$$l = \{(x,y) \in \mathbb{R}^2 : y = 1 - x\}.$$

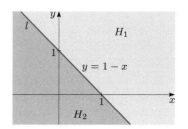

This line splits $\mathbb{R}^2$ into three separate parts: the line l itself, the set H_1 of points lying *above* the line, and the set H_2 of points lying *below* the line.

Consider an arbitrary point $P = (x,y)$ in H_1 as shown in the margin. The point $Q = (x, 1-x)$ lies on the line l, below P, as illustrated, so $y > 1-x$. Similarly, each point (x,y) in H_2 satisfies $y < 1-x$. Thus

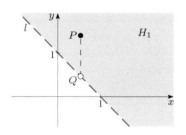

$$H_1 = \{(x,y) \in \mathbb{R}^2 : y > 1 - x\}$$

and

$$H_2 = \{(x,y) \in \mathbb{R}^2 : y < 1 - x\}.$$

(In the diagrams, when a plane set illustrated does not include a boundary line, we draw the boundary line as a broken line.)

The set of points on one side of a line, possibly together with all the points on the line itself, is known as a **half-plane**. A half-plane that does not include the points on the line can be specified using set notation in a similar way to the examples H_1 and H_2 above. The corresponding half-plane that includes the points on the line can be specified by changing the symbol $>$ to $\geq$, or the symbol $<$ to $\leq$.

Next consider the unit circle

$$U = \{(x,y) \in \mathbb{R}^2 : x^2 + y^2 = 1\}.$$

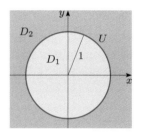

This circle splits $\mathbb{R}^2$ into three separate parts: the circle U itself, the set D_1 of points lying *inside* the circle and the set D_2 of points lying *outside* the circle.

The condition for a point (x,y) to lie inside U is that the distance from the origin is less than 1, so the square of the distance is also less than 1. Thus

$$D_1 = \{(x,y) \in \mathbb{R}^2 : x^2 + y^2 < 1\}.$$

Similarly,

$$D_2 = \{(x,y) \in \mathbb{R}^2 : x^2 + y^2 > 1\}.$$

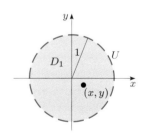

The set of points inside a circle, possibly together with all the points on the circle, is known as a **disc**. If we wish to specify the disc consisting of the unit circle and the points inside it, we replace the inequality $<$ by $\leq$ in the set notation specification of D_1 given above.

Now consider the set of points lying inside the square with vertices $(0,0)$, $(1,0)$, $(1,1)$ and $(0,1)$. This set can be written as

$$\{(x,y) \in \mathbb{R}^2 : 0 < x < 1,\ 0 < y < 1\}.$$

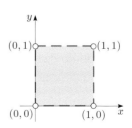

If we wish to include the four boundary lines in the set, we replace each symbol $<$ by $\leq$. We would show this set on a diagram by replacing the broken lines in the diagram in the margin by solid lines.

Exercise 1.6   Sketch each of the following plane sets.

(a) $\{(x,y) \in \mathbb{R}^2 : x < 1\}$

(b) $\{(x,y) \in \mathbb{R}^2 : y < 2 - 2x\}$

(c) $\{(x,y) \in \mathbb{R}^2 : (x-1)^2 + (y-2)^2 \leq 4\}$

(d) $\{(x,y) \in \mathbb{R}^2 : x^2 + (y+3)^2 > 1\}$

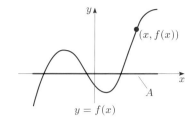

We conclude this subsection by considering the graph of a real function. In Unit I1, we sketched the graph of a real function f by plotting points of the form $(x, f(x))$ in $\mathbb{R}^2$, for each element x of the domain A. This suggests the following formal definition of a graph.

Definition   The **graph** of a real function $f : A \longrightarrow \mathbb{R}$ is the set
$$\{(x, f(x)) : x \in A\}.$$

Exercise 1.7   Use set notation to specify:

(a) the points in the square with vertices $(0, 1)$, $(2, 1)$, $(2, 3)$, $(0, 3)$, if the boundary is included;

(b) the points on the graph of the function
$$f : [0, \infty) \longrightarrow \mathbb{R}$$
$$x \longmapsto 2x^2 + 1.$$

1.4 Set equality and subsets

Consider the sets $A = \{1, -1\}$ and $B = \{x \in \mathbb{R} : x^2 - 1 = 0\}$. Although these sets are written in different ways, each set contains exactly the same elements, 1 and -1. We say that these sets are *equal*.

Definition   Two sets A and B are **equal** if they have exactly the same elements; we write $A = B$.

When two sets each contain a small number of elements, we can usually check whether these elements are the same, and hence decide whether the sets are equal.

Exercise 1.8   Decide whether each of the following pairs of sets are equal.

(a) $A = \{2, -3\}$ and $B = \{x \in \mathbb{R} : x^2 + x - 6 = 0\}$.

(b) $A = \{k \in \mathbb{Z} : k \text{ is odd and } 2 < k < 10\}$ and $B = \{n \in \mathbb{N} : n \text{ is a prime number and } n < 10\}$.

If two sets each contain more than a small number of elements, it is less easy to check whether they are equal. We shall describe a method for dealing with cases like this after we have introduced an idea that we shall need.

Consider the sets $A = \{7, 2, 5\}$ and $B = \{2, 3, 5, 7, 11\}$. Each element of A is also an element of B. We say that A is a *subset* of B.

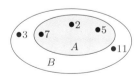

Definition   A set A is a **subset** of a set B if each element of A is also an element of B. We also say that A is **contained in** B, and we write $A \subseteq B$.

We sometimes indicate that a set A is a subset of a set B by reversing the symbol $\subseteq$ and writing $B \supseteq A$, which we read as 'B **contains** A'. To indicate that A is *not* a subset of B, we write $A \nsubseteq B$. We may also write this as $B \nsupseteq A$, which we read as 'B does not contain A'.

Do not confuse the symbol $\subseteq$ with the symbol $\in$. For example, we write
$$\{1\} \subseteq \{1, 2, 3\},$$
since $\{1\}$ is a *subset* of $\{1,2,3\}$, and
$$1 \in \{1, 2, 3\},$$
since 1 is an *element* of $\{1,2,3\}$.

11

When we wish to determine whether a given set A is a subset of a given set B, the method that we use depends on the way in which the two sets are defined. If A has a small number of elements, then we check directly by inspection whether each element of A is an element of B. Otherwise, we determine whether an arbitrary element of A fulfils the membership criteria for B, as illustrated by Example 1.2 below.

To show that a given set A is *not* a subset of a given set B, we need to find at least one element of A that does not belong to B. The empty set $\varnothing$ is a subset of *every* set because we cannot find an element in $\varnothing$ which does not belong to the set in question.

Example 1.2   In each of the following cases, determine whether $A \subseteq B$.

(a) $A = \{1, 2, -4\}$ and $B = \{x \in \mathbb{R} : x^5 + 4x^4 - x - 4 = 0\}$.

(b) $A = \{(x, y) \in \mathbb{R}^2 : x^2 + y^2 < 1\}$ and $B = \{(x, y) \in \mathbb{R}^2 : x < 1\}$.

Solution

(a) The elements 1, 2, -4 belong to $\mathbb{R}$, and we can check directly whether they also satisfy the equation $x^5 + 4x^4 - x - 4 = 0$. We have

$$(1)^5 + 4(1)^4 - 1 - 4 = 0, \quad \text{so } 1 \in B,$$

$$(2)^5 + 4(2)^4 - 2 - 4 = 90, \quad \text{so } 2 \notin B.$$

Since $2 \notin B$, we do not need to check whether $-4 \in B$.

So 2 does not belong to B, and hence A is not contained in B.

(b) From the diagram in the margin, it appears that $A \subseteq B$. We cannot check each of the elements of A individually, so we let (x, y) be an arbitrary element of A; then (x, y) is a point of $\mathbb{R}^2$ with $x^2 + y^2 < 1$.

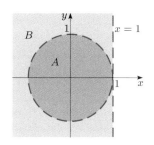

Since $y^2 \geq 0$ for all y, this implies that $x^2 < 1$, and hence that $x < 1$. Thus $(x, y) \in B$.

Since (x, y) is an arbitrary element of A, we conclude that $A \subseteq B$. ∎

Exercise 1.9 In each of the following cases, determine whether $A \subseteq B$.

(a) $A = \{(5, 2), (1, 1), (-3, 0)\}$ and $B = \{(x, y) \in \mathbb{R}^2 : x - 4y = -3\}$.

(b) $A = \{(x, y) \in \mathbb{R}^2 : x^2 + y^2 < 1\}$ and $B = \{(x, y) \in \mathbb{R}^2 : y < 0\}$.

If two sets A and B are equal, then A is a subset of B, and B is a subset of A. If a set A is a subset of a set B that is not equal to B, then we say that A is a **proper subset** of B, and we write $A \subset B$ or $B \supset A$.

In some texts, the symbol $\subset$ is used to mean 'is a subset of' (for which we use the symbol $\subseteq$) rather than 'is a proper subset of'.

To show that a set A is a proper subset of a set B, we must show both that A is a subset of B, and that there is at least one element of B that is not an element of A.

Example 1.3   Show that A is a proper subset of B, where A and B are the sets defined in Example 1.2(b).

Solution   We showed in the solution to Example 1.2(b) that $A \subseteq B$. Also, the point $(0, 2)$, for example, lies in B, since its x-coordinate 0 is less than 1, but $(0, 2)$ does not lie in A, since $0^2 + 2^2 = 4 \geq 1$. This shows that A is a proper subset of B. ∎

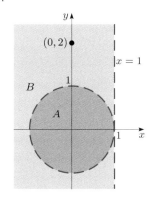

Exercise 1.10 Show that A is a proper subset of B, where A and B are the sets defined in Exercise 1.9(a).

We now return to the question of how we can show that two sets A and B are equal if they have more than a small number of elements. To do this, we show that each set is a subset of the other.

Strategy 1.1   To show that two sets A and B are equal:

show that $A \subseteq B$;

show that $B \subseteq A$.

Example 1.4   Show that the following sets are equal:

$$A = \{(\cos t, \sin t) : t \in [0, 2\pi]\} \quad \text{and} \quad B = \{(x, y) \in \mathbb{R}^2 : x^2 + y^2 = 1\}.$$

Solution   First we show that $A \subseteq B$.

Let (x, y) be an arbitrary element of A; then

$$x = \cos t \quad \text{and} \quad y = \sin t, \quad \text{for some } t \in [0, 2\pi],$$

so

$$x^2 + y^2 = \cos^2 t + \sin^2 t = 1.$$

This implies that $(x, y) \in B$, so $A \subseteq B$.

Next we show that $B \subseteq A$.

Let (x, y) be an arbitrary element of B; then

$$x^2 + y^2 = 1.$$

In order to show that (x, y) is an element of A, we need to find a value of $t \in [0, 2\pi]$ such that $(x, y) = (\cos t, \sin t)$. If we take t to be the angle between the x-axis and the line joining the point (x, y) to the origin, then

$$x = \cos t \quad \text{and} \quad y = \sin t.$$

Since $t \in [0, 2\pi]$, it follows that $(x, y) \in A$, so $B \subseteq A$.

Since $A \subseteq B$ and $B \subseteq A$, it follows that $A = B$.   ∎

Exercise 1.11   Show that the following sets are equal:

$$A = \{(t^2, 2t) : t \in \mathbb{R}\} \quad \text{and} \quad B = \{(x, y) \in \mathbb{R}^2 : y^2 = 4x\}.$$

In Unit I1, Section 5, you saw that

$$\alpha(t) = (\cos t, \sin t), \quad t \in [0, 2\pi],$$

is a parametrisation of the unit circle, so we expect A and B to be the same set.

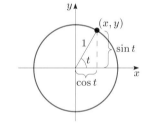

1.5 Counting subsets of finite sets

A *finite* set is a set which has a *finite* number of elements; that is, the number of elements is some natural number, or 0. We saw earlier that in using set notation, we may list the elements of a finite set in any order. For example, the set $\{1, 2, 3\}$ can be written by ordering the elements in six different ways:

$$\{1, 2, 3\}, \ \{1, 3, 2\}, \ \{2, 1, 3\}, \ \{2, 3, 1\}, \ \{3, 1, 2\}, \ \{3, 2, 1\}$$

(with each element of the set specified just once).

In general, a set with n elements can be ordered in

$$n \times (n - 1) \times \cdots \times 1 \tag{1.1}$$

different ways, as there are n choices for the first element, then $n - 1$ choices for the second element, and so on, with just one possibility for the last element.

The number of elements is 0 in the case of the empty set $\varnothing$.

We denote expression (1.1) by $n!$ (read as 'n factorial').

Definition For any positive integer n,

$$n! = n \times (n-1) \times (n-2) \times \cdots \times 3 \times 2 \times 1.$$

Also,

$$0! = 1.$$

For example, a set with 10 elements can be ordered in

$$10! = 10 \times 9 \times \cdots \times 1 = 3\,628\,800$$

different ways.

A finite set has only finitely many subsets—but how many? Consider, for example, the set $\{1,2,3\}$. Below, we list all the subsets of $\{1,2,3\}$ in a table, according to the size k of the subsets.

k	subsets of $\{1,2,3\}$	number of subsets
0	$\varnothing$	1
1	$\{1\}$, $\{2\}$, $\{3\}$	3
2	$\{1,2\}$, $\{1,3\}$, $\{2,3\}$	3
3	$\{1,2,3\}$	1

This table shows that the set $\{1,2,3\}$ has $1+3+3+1 = 8$ subsets in all.

Exercise 1.12 List all the subsets of the set $\{1,2,3,4\}$ in a similar table.

We have seen that a set with 3 elements has 8 subsets and a set with 4 elements has 16 subsets. This suggests that a set with n elements has 2^n subsets. To see this, we can argue as follows. Given a set A with n elements, we can associate with each subset of A a string of n symbols, where the kth symbol is a 1 if the kth element of A is in the subset, and a 0 otherwise. For example, if $A = \{1,2,3,4,5\}$, then the string associated with the subset $\{2,4,5\}$ is 01011. There are 2^n such strings (since there are 2 choices for each of the n symbols), so there are 2^n subsets.

We now concentrate on the following related question.

> How many subsets with k elements has a set with n elements?

To answer this question, we consider choosing the k elements of the subset in order. There are n choices for the first element of the subset, then $n-1$ choices for the second element, and so on, with $n-(k-1) = n-k+1$ choices for the kth element. Hence the number of ways of choosing k elements *in order* from n elements is

$$n \times (n-1) \times \cdots \times (n-k+1).$$

But some of these $n \times (n-1) \times \cdots \times (n-k+1)$ *ordered* choices give rise to the same subset. In fact, each subset of k elements corresponds to $k!$ ordered choices of k elements. Thus the number of *different* subsets with k elements of a set with n elements is

$$\frac{n \times (n-1) \times \cdots \times (n-k+1)}{k!}.$$

We define 0! to be 1 for convenience, so that results such as $n! = n \times (n-1)!$ are also true for $n = 1$. Also, this definition makes sense because the number of different orderings of the elements of the empty set is 1; we cannot change the order of no elements!

Multiplying the numerator and denominator by $(n - k)!$, we obtain

$$\frac{n!}{k!\,(n - k)!}.$$

We introduce the following notation for this expression.

Definition   For any non-negative integers n and k with $k \leq n$,

$$\binom{n}{k} = \frac{n!}{k!\,(n - k)!}.$$

This expression is called a **binomial coefficient**. It is the number of subsets with k elements of a set with n elements.

The expression $\binom{n}{k}$ is read as 'n choose k'. Some texts use the alternative notation ${}^nC_k$, where the 'C' stands for 'combination'. The reason for the name 'binomial coefficient' will become clear in Section 4.

For example, the number of subsets with two elements of a set with three elements is

$$\binom{3}{2} = \frac{3!}{2!\,1!} = 3,$$

as we found in the table on page 14.

A more interesting example is that of a lottery in which participants choose a subset of six numbers from a set of 49 numbers. In this case there are

$$\binom{49}{6} = \frac{49!}{6!\,43!} = \frac{49 \times 48 \times 47 \times 46 \times 45 \times 44}{6 \times 5 \times 4 \times 3 \times 2 \times 1} = 13\,983\,816$$

different subsets, or *combinations* as they are commonly called.

We can of course drop the '$\times 1$' in the denominator and write
$$\frac{49 \times 48 \times 47 \times 46 \times 45 \times 44}{6 \times 5 \times 4 \times 3 \times 2}.$$

Exercise 1.13   Evaluate $\binom{10}{2}$, $\binom{10}{3}$ and $\binom{11}{3}$, and verify that

$$\binom{10}{2} + \binom{10}{3} = \binom{11}{3}.$$

The result of Exercise 1.13 is a special case of the following general result.

Example 1.5   Prove that that if n and k are positive integers with $1 \leq k \leq n$, then

$$\binom{n}{k - 1} + \binom{n}{k} = \binom{n + 1}{k}.$$

We use this identity in Section 4.

Solution   We start with the left-hand side and use successive rearrangements to obtain the right-hand side:

$$\binom{n}{k - 1} + \binom{n}{k} = \frac{n!}{(k - 1)!\,(n - (k - 1))!} + \frac{n!}{k!\,(n - k)!}$$

$$= \frac{kn!}{k(k - 1)!\,(n - k + 1)!} + \frac{(n - k + 1)n!}{k!\,(n - k)!\,(n - k + 1)}$$

$$= \frac{kn!}{k!\,(n - k + 1)!} + \frac{(n - k + 1)n!}{k!\,(n - k + 1)!}$$

$$= \frac{(k + (n - k + 1)) \times n!}{k!\,(n - k + 1)!}$$

$$= \frac{(n + 1) \times n!}{k!\,(n - k + 1)!}$$

$$= \frac{(n + 1)!}{k!\,(n + 1 - k)!} = \binom{n + 1}{k}. \quad \blacksquare$$

We can give an alternative proof of the above identity by interpreting the left- and right-hand sides as the results obtained by counting the same thing in two different ways. If we deem one of $n + 1$ elements to be the first, then the $\binom{n+1}{k}$ subsets of k elements chosen from these $n + 1$ elements consist of $\binom{n}{k-1}$ subsets which include the first element (and $k - 1$ other elements), and $\binom{n}{k}$ subsets which do not include the first element.

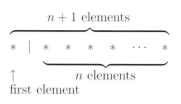

Such a *combinatorial* or *counting argument* can be spotted only with practice.

Exercise 1.14 Prove the following identity (a) directly, (b) by using a combinatorial argument.

If n and k are positive integers with $0 \le k \le n$, then
$$\binom{n}{n-k} = \binom{n}{k}.$$

1.6 Set operations

Consider the two sets $\{2, 3, 5\}$ and $\{1, 2, 5, 8\}$. Using these sets, we can construct several new sets—for example:

- the set $\{1, 2, 3, 5, 8\}$ consisting of all elements belonging to *at least one* of the two sets;
- the set $\{2, 5\}$ consisting of all elements belonging to *both* of the two sets;
- the set $\{3\}$ consisting of all elements belonging to the first set but not the second, and the set $\{1, 8\}$ consisting of all elements belonging to the second set but not the first.

Each of these new sets is a particular instance of a general construction for sets. We now consider them in turn.

Union

We saw above that if $A = \{2, 3, 5\}$ and $B = \{1, 2, 5, 8\}$, then the set of all elements belonging to at least one of the sets A and B is $\{1, 2, 3, 5, 8\}$. We call this set the *union* of A and B.

More generally, we adopt the following definition.

> **Definition**   Let A and B be any two sets; then the **union** of A and B is the set
> $$A \cup B = \{x : x \in A \text{ or } x \in B\}.$$

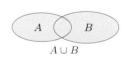

$A \cup B$

Note that the word *or* in this definition is used in the inclusive sense of 'and/or'; that is, the set $A \cup B$ consists of the elements of A and the elements of B, including the elements in both A and B.

In everyday language, an example of 'or' used in the *exclusive* sense is 'Tea or coffee?', since the answer 'Both, please!' is not expected. An example of 'or' used in the *inclusive* sense is 'Milk or sugar?', since in this case you could answer 'Both'.

Example 1.6

(a) Simplify $[-2, 4] \cup (0, 10)$.

(b) Express the domain of the function $f(x) = \sqrt{x^2 - 1}$ as a union of intervals.

Solution

(a) The union is the interval $[-2, 10)$.

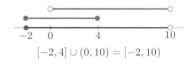

$[-2, 4] \cup (0, 10) = [-2, 10)$

(b) The domain consists of all real numbers x for which $x^2 - 1 \geq 0$: that is, $x^2 \geq 1$, so $x \geq 1$ or $x \leq -1$. Thus the domain of f is the set

$$\{x \in \mathbb{R} : x \leq -1 \text{ or } x \geq 1\}.$$

This is the set of numbers belonging either to the interval $(-\infty, -1]$ or to the interval $[1, \infty)$, and it can therefore be written as

$$(-\infty, -1] \cup [1, \infty). \quad \blacksquare$$

$(-\infty, -1] \cup [1, \infty)$

Exercise 1.15

(a) Simplify $(1, 7) \cup [4, 11]$.

(b) Express the domain of the function $f(x) = 1/\sqrt{x^2 - 9}$ as a union of intervals.

(c) Draw a diagram depicting the union of the half-plane $H = \{(x, y) \in \mathbb{R}^2 : y < 0\}$ and the disc $D = \{(x, y) \in \mathbb{R}^2 : x^2 + y^2 \leq 4\}$.

So far we have defined the union of two sets. We can give a similar definition for the union of any number of sets; for example, the union of three sets A, B and C is the set

$$A \cup B \cup C = \{x : x \in A \text{ or } x \in B \text{ or } x \in C\}.$$

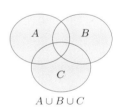

$A \cup B \cup C$

Intersection

We saw above that if $A = \{2, 3, 5\}$ and $B = \{1, 2, 5, 8\}$, then the set of all elements belonging to both of the sets A and B is $\{2, 5\}$. We call this set the *intersection* of A and B.

More generally, we adopt the following definition.

Definition   Let A and B be any two sets; then the **intersection** of A and B is the set

$$A \cap B = \{x : x \in A \text{ and } x \in B\}.$$

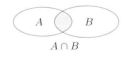

$A \cap B$

Two sets with no element in common, such as $\{1, 3, 5\}$ and $\{2, 9\}$, are said to be **disjoint**. We write $\{1, 3, 5\} \cap \{2, 9\} = \varnothing$.

Example 1.7

(a) Simplify $[-2, 4] \cap (0, 10)$.

(b) Express the domain of the function $f(x) = 1/\sqrt{4 - x^2} + 1/\sqrt{9 - x^2}$ as an intersection of intervals, and simplify your answer.

Solution

(a) The intersection is the interval $(0, 4]$.

(b) The domain consists of all real numbers x for which both $4 - x^2 > 0$
and $9 - x^2 > 0$; that is, $x^2 < 4$ and $x^2 < 9$. Thus the domain of f is
the set of real numbers x that belong both to the interval $(-2, 2)$ and
to the interval $(-3, 3)$. It can therefore be written as

$$(-2, 2) \cap (-3, 3);$$

this is simply the interval $(-2, 2)$.   ■

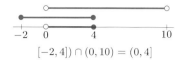

$[-2, 4]) \cap (0, 10) = (0, 4]$

Exercise 1.16

(a) Simplify $(1, 7) \cap [4, 11]$.

(b) Draw a diagram depicting the intersection of the half-plane
$H = \{(x, y) \in \mathbb{R}^2 : y < 0\}$ and the disc
$D = \{(x, y) \in \mathbb{R}^2 : x^2 + y^2 \leq 4\}$.

So far we have defined the intersection of two sets. We can give a similar
definition for the intersection of any number of sets; for example, the
intersection of three sets A, B and C is the set

$$A \cap B \cap C = \{x : x \in A \text{ and } x \in B \text{ and } x \in C\}.$$

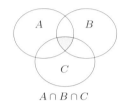

$A \cap B \cap C$

Difference

We saw above that if $A = \{2, 3, 5\}$ and $B = \{1, 2, 5, 8\}$, then the set of all
elements belonging to A but not to B is $\{3\}$; we call this set the
difference $A - B$. Similarly, the set of all elements belonging to B but not
to A is $\{1, 8\}$; this set is the *difference* $B - A$.

More generally, we adopt the following definition.

Definition   Let A and B be any two sets; then the **difference**
between A and B is the set

$$A - B = \{x : x \in A, \ x \notin B\}.$$

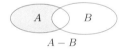

$A - B$

Some texts denote the difference
between A and B by $A \setminus B$.

Remark   Note that $A - B$ is different from $B - A$, when $A \neq B$. Also, for
any set A, we have $A - A = \varnothing$.

Example 1.8

(a) Simplify $[-2, 4] - (0, 10)$ and $(0, 10) - [-2, 4]$.

(b) Express the domain of the function $f(x) = 1/(x^2 - 1)$ as a difference
between two sets.

Solution

(a) The difference $[-2, 4] - (0, 10)$ is the interval $[-2, 0]$, and the difference
$(0, 10) - [-2, 4]$ is $(4, 10)$.

(b) The domain consists of all real numbers x for which $x^2 - 1 \neq 0$; that
is, $x \neq 1$ and $x \neq -1$. Thus the domain of f is the difference

$$\mathbb{R} - \{1, -1\}. \quad ■$$

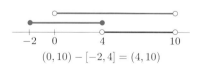

$(0, 10) - [-2, 4] = (4, 10)$

Exercise 1.17

(a) Simplify $(1, 7) - [4, 11]$ and $[4, 11] - (1, 7)$.

(b) Draw diagrams depicting $H - D$ and $D - H$, where H is the half-plane $\{(x, y) \in \mathbb{R}^2 : y < 0\}$ and D is the disc $\{(x, y) \in \mathbb{R}^2 : x^2 + y^2 \leq 4\}$.

Further exercises

Exercise 1.18   Which of the following statements are true?

(a) $0 \in \mathbb{N}$ (b) $0 \in \mathbb{Q}$ (c) $-0.6 \notin \mathbb{R}$ (d) $37 \in \mathbb{Z}$

(e) $20 \in \{4, 8, 12, 16\}$ (f) $\{1, 2\} \in \{\{2, 3\}, \{3, 1\}, \{2, 1\}\}$

(g) $\{0\} \in \varnothing$

Exercise 1.19   List the elements of the following sets.

(a) $\{n : n \in \mathbb{N} \text{ and } 2 < n < 7\}$ (b) $\{x \in \mathbb{R} : x^2 + 5x + 4 = 0\}$

(c) $\{n \in \mathbb{N} : n^2 = 25\}$

Exercise 1.20   Use set notation to specify each of the following sets:

(a) the set of integers greater than -20 and less than -3;

(b) the set of non-zero integers which are multiples of 3;

(c) the set of all real numbers greater than 15.

Exercise 1.21   Sketch the following sets in $\mathbb{R}^2$.

(a) $\{(x, y) \in \mathbb{R}^2 : y = 4 - 3x\}$

(b) $\{(x, y) \in \mathbb{R}^2 : (x + 1)^2 + (y - 3)^2 = 9\}$

(c) $\{(x, y) \in \mathbb{R}^2 : y^2 = 8x\}$

Exercise 1.22   Sketch the following sets in $\mathbb{R}^2$.

(a) $\{(x, y) \in \mathbb{R}^2 : y < 4 - 3x\}$

(b) $\{(x, y) \in \mathbb{R}^2 : (x + 1)^2 + (y - 3)^2 > 9\}$

(c) $\{(x, y) \in \mathbb{R}^2 : 0 \leq x \leq 2, \ 1 \leq y \leq 3\}$

Exercise 1.23   For each of the sets A and B below, determine whether $A \subseteq B$.

(a) $A = \{(0, 0), (0, 6), (-4, 6)\}$ and
    $B = \{(x, y) \in \mathbb{R}^2 : (x + 2)^2 + (y - 3)^2 = 13\}$.

(b) $A = \{(x, y) \in \mathbb{R}^2 : x^2 + y^2 < 4\}$ and $B = \{(x, y) \in \mathbb{R}^2 : y < 4 - 8x\}$.

(c) $A = \{(2\cos t, 3\sin t) : t \in [0, 2\pi]\}$ and $B = \{(x, y) \in \mathbb{R}^2 : \dfrac{x^2}{4} + \dfrac{y^2}{9} = 1\}$.

Exercise 1.24   Show that A is a proper subset of B, where

$A = \{(x, y) \in \mathbb{R}^2 : x^2 + 4y^2 < 1\}$ and $B = \{(x, y) \in \mathbb{R}^2 : y < \frac{1}{2}\}$.

Exercise 1.25   For each of the sets A and B below, determine whether $A = B$.

(a) $A = \{1, -1, 2\}$ and $B = \{x \in \mathbb{R} : x^3 - 2x^2 - x + 2 = 0\}$.

(b) $A = \{(2\cos t, 3\sin t) : t \in [0, 2\pi]\}$ and

$B = \{(x, y) \in \mathbb{R}^2 : \dfrac{x^2}{4} + \dfrac{y^2}{9} = 1\}$.

(c) $A = \{x \in \mathbb{R} : x = \dfrac{p}{q}, \text{ where } p, q \in \mathbb{N}\}$ and $B = \mathbb{Q}$.

Exercise 1.26   For each of the sets A and B below, find $A \cup B$, $A \cap B$ and $A - B$.

(a) $A = \{0, 2, 4\}$ and $B = \{4, 5, 6\}$.

(b) $A = (-5, 3]$ and $B = [2, 17]$.

(c) $A = \{(x, y) \in \mathbb{R}^2 : x^2 + y^2 \leq 1\}$ and $B = \{(x, y) \in \mathbb{R}^2 : x^2 + y^2 \leq 4\}$.

2   Functions

After working through this section, you should be able to:

(a) determine the *image* of a given function;

(b) determine whether a given function is *one-one* and/or *onto*;

(c) find the *inverse* of a given one-one function;

(d) find the *composite* of two given functions.

2.1   What is a function?

In the previous unit we concentrated on *real* functions—that is, functions whose domains and codomains are subsets of $\mathbb{R}$. You can think of these functions as machines for processing real numbers. For example, the real function defined by $f(x) = 1/x$ can be regarded as a machine that calculates the reciprocals of non-zero real numbers. When 3 is fed into the machine, out comes the number $\frac{1}{3}$; when -2 is fed into the machine, out comes $-\frac{1}{2}$; and so on. Indeed, any real number in the domain $\mathbb{R}^*$ of f can be processed by the machine to produce a real number in the codomain.

Recall from Subsection 1.1 that $\mathbb{R}^*$ denotes the set of non-zero real numbers, $\mathbb{R} - \{0\}$.

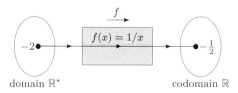

domain $\mathbb{R}^*$ codomain $\mathbb{R}$

Now imagine a machine that accepts an element x from a set A (not necessarily a subset of $\mathbb{R}$), and processes it to produce a unique element $f(x)$ in a set B (again not necessarily a subset of $\mathbb{R}$). By dropping the requirement that the machine processes and produces real numbers, we obtain the following more general definition of a function.

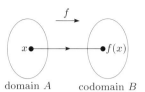

Definitions A **function** f is defined by specifying:

- a set A, called the **domain** of f;
- a set B, called the **codomain** of f;
- a **rule** $x \longmapsto f(x)$ that associates with each element $x \in A$ a unique element $f(x) \in B$.

The element $f(x)$ is the **image** of x under f.

Symbolically, we write

$$f : A \longrightarrow B$$
$$x \longmapsto f(x).$$

We often refer to a function as a **mapping**, and say that f **maps** A to B and x to $f(x)$.

Since the domain A and the codomain B are no longer restricted to be sets of real numbers, we can now study many types of function in addition to the real functions that you met in Unit I1. We present a few examples.

Distance function

Functions of the form $f : \mathbb{R}^2 \longrightarrow \mathbb{R}$ can be used to specify quantities associated with points in the plane. For example, the function

$$f : \mathbb{R}^2 \longrightarrow \mathbb{R}$$
$$(x, y) \longmapsto \sqrt{x^2 + y^2}$$

gives the distance of each point (x, y) in the plane from the origin.

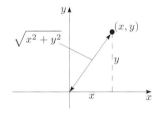

Parametrisations

In Unit I1, Section 5, you saw that functions of the form $f : I \longrightarrow \mathbb{R}^2$, where I is an interval of $\mathbb{R}$, can be used to parametrise curves in the plane. For example, the function

$$f : [0, 2\pi] \longrightarrow \mathbb{R}^2$$
$$t \longmapsto (\cos t, \sin t)$$

is a parametrisation of the unit circle.

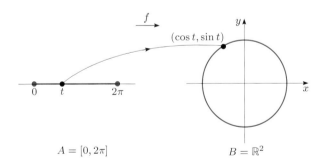

Transformations of the plane

Functions that have a geometric interpretation are often called *transformations*. Such functions include translations, reflections and rotations of the plane. We now present some simple examples. For each one, we give a diagram which shows the effect of the transformation on the square whose vertices are at $(0,0)$, $(1,0)$, $(1,1)$ and $(0,1)$; part of the square is shaded for clarity.

These types of transformation were introduced in Unit I1, Section 1, Frames 10, 18 and 20. You will study more complicated transformations in the Linear Algebra Block.

21

The transformation

$$f : \mathbb{R}^2 \longrightarrow \mathbb{R}^2$$
$$(x, y) \longmapsto (x + 2, y)$$

is a *translation* of the plane that shifts (or translates) each point to the right by 2 units.

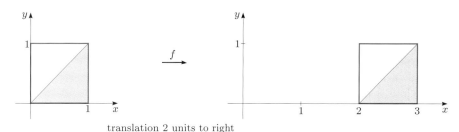

translation 2 units to right

The transformation

$$f : \mathbb{R}^2 \longrightarrow \mathbb{R}^2$$
$$(x, y) \longmapsto (-x, y)$$

is a *reflection* of the plane in the y-axis.

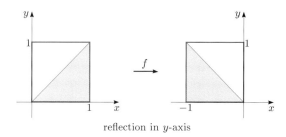

reflection in y-axis

The transformation

$$f : \mathbb{R}^2 \longrightarrow \mathbb{R}^2$$
$$(x, y) \longmapsto (-x, -y)$$

is a *rotation* of the plane through π about the origin.

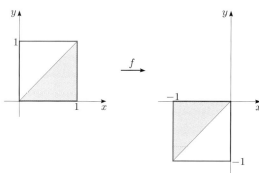

rotation through π about origin

Exercise 2.1   For each of the following functions $f : \mathbb{R}^2 \longrightarrow \mathbb{R}^2$, state whether f is a translation, reflection or rotation of the plane.

(a) $f(x, y) = (x + 2, y + 3)$

(b) $f(x, y) = (x, -y)$

(c) $f(x, y) = (-y, x)$

For simplicity, we write $f(x, y)$ instead of $f((x, y))$.

Functions on finite sets

It is often useful to consider a function whose domain is a *finite* set. For example, we can define a function whose domain is the set

$$A = \{0, 1, 2, 3, 4, 5, 6, 7, 8, 9\}$$

by

$$f : A \longrightarrow A$$
$$x \longmapsto 9 - x.$$

When the domain of a function f has a small number of elements, we can specify the rule of f by listing the image $f(x)$ of each element x in the domain. For example, let $A = \{0, 1, 2, 3\}$ and $B = \{2, 3, 4, 5\}$; then we can define a function $f : A \longrightarrow B$ by the rule

$$f(0) = 2, \quad f(1) = 2, \quad f(2) = 4, \quad f(3) = 5.$$

We can represent the behaviour of this function by a diagram, as shown below.

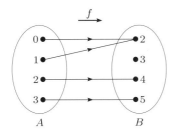

There is exactly *one* arrow *from* each element in the domain, since each element in the domain has exactly *one* image in the codomain. There may be no arrows, one arrow or several arrows going *to* an element in the codomain, since an element in the codomain may not be an image at all, may be an image of exactly one element in the domain, or may be an image of several elements in the domain.

For example, for this function, 3 is not an image at all, 5 is the image of 3 only, and 2 is the image of both 0 and 1.

Exercise 2.2   Which of the following diagrams correspond(s) to a function?

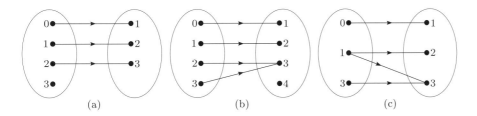

Identity functions

Associated with any set A, there is a particularly simple function whose domain and codomain are the set A. This is the *identity function* i_A which maps each element of A to itself.

We sometimes omit the subscript A if we do not need to emphasise the set.

For example, let $A = \{0, 1, 2, 3\}$; then the rule of the identity function is

$$i_A(0) = 0, \quad i_A(1) = 1, \quad i_A(2) = 2, \quad i_A(3) = 3.$$

The following definition applies to *any* set A, finite or infinite.

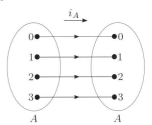

> **Definition**   The **identity function** on a set A is the function
>
> $$i_A : A \longrightarrow A$$
> $$x \longmapsto x.$$

2.2 Image of a function

The rule associated with a function tells us how to find the image of any element in the domain. Often, however, we need to consider the images of a whole subset of elements drawn from the domain; for example, in geometry, we frequently wish to consider the effect of a transformation on a plane figure, a subset of $\mathbb{R}^2$.

> **Definition**   Given a function $f : A \longrightarrow B$, and a subset S of A, the **image**, or **image set**, of S under f, written $f(S)$, is the set
>
> $$f(S) = \{f(x) : x \in S\}.$$

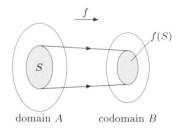

domain A codomain B

For example, suppose that S is the square with vertices at $(0,0)$, $(1,0)$, $(1,1)$ and $(0,1)$, and we want to find the image of S under the function

$$f : \mathbb{R}^2 \longrightarrow \mathbb{R}^2$$
$$(x,y) \longmapsto (x+2,y).$$

This function is the translation of the plane which moves each point (x,y) to the right by 2. The image of S is therefore the square with vertices at $f(0,0) = (2,0)$, $f(1,0) = (3,0)$, $f(1,1) = (3,1)$ and $f(0,1) = (2,1)$.

Sometimes we wish to consider the image of the *whole domain* of a function: this is referred to as the image, or image set, of the *function*.

> **Definition**   The **image**, or **image set**, of a function $f : A \longrightarrow B$ is the set
>
> $$f(A) = \{f(x) : x \in A\}.$$

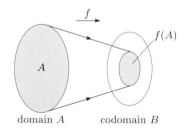

domain A codomain B

The image of a function is a subset of its codomain. It need not be *equal* to the codomain because there may be some elements of the codomain that are not images of elements in the domain.

When the domain of a function f has a small number of elements, we can find the image of f by finding the image of each element in the domain, and listing them to form a set.

Example 2.1   Let $A = \{0,1,2,3,4,5,6,7,8,9\}$.

Find the image of the function

$$f : A \longrightarrow A$$
$$x \longmapsto \left[\tfrac{1}{2}x\right].$$

Recall that $[x]$, the *integer part* of x, is the largest integer that is less than or equal to x. For example, $[3.7] = 3$, $[3] = 3$ and $[-3.7] = -4$.

Solution   The images of the elements of A are

$f(0) = 0, \quad f(1) = 0, \quad f(2) = 1, \quad f(3) = 1, \quad f(4) = 2,$
$f(5) = 2, \quad f(6) = 3, \quad f(7) = 3, \quad f(8) = 4, \quad f(9) = 4.$

So the image of f is $f(A) = \{0, 1, 2, 3, 4\}$.   ■

Exercise 2.3   Let $A = \{0, 1, 2, 3, 4, 5, 6, 7, 8, 9\}$.

Find the image of the function

$$f : A \longrightarrow A$$
$$x \longmapsto 9 - x.$$

In Exercise 2.3 you should have found that the image and the codomain coincide. In other words, each element of the codomain is the image of an element in the domain. A function with this property is said to be *onto*.

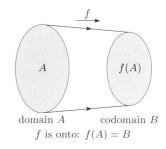

domain A codomain B
f is onto: $f(A) = B$

Definition   A function $f : A \longrightarrow B$ is **onto** if $f(A) = B$.

Exercise 2.4   Which of the following diagrams correspond(s) to an onto function?

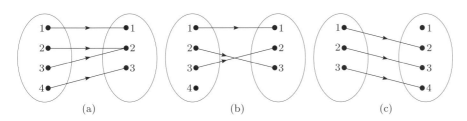

       (a)   (b)   (c)

Example 2.2   For each of the following functions, find its image and determine whether it is onto.

Some texts refer to an onto function as a *surjective* function.

(a) $f : \mathbb{R} \longrightarrow \mathbb{R}$ (b) $f : \mathbb{R} \longrightarrow \mathbb{R}$ (c) $f : \mathbb{R}^2 \longrightarrow \mathbb{R}^2$
    $x \longmapsto 2x - 5$ $x \longmapsto x^2$ $(x, y) \longmapsto (x + 1, y + 2)$

(d) $f : A \longrightarrow A, \quad$ where $A = \{0, 1, 2, 3, 4, 5, 6, 7, 8, 9\}$
    $x \longmapsto \left[\frac{1}{2}x\right]$

Solution

(a) The sketch of the graph of f shown in the margin suggests that the image of f is the whole of $\mathbb{R}$. To confirm this, we prove algebraically that $f(\mathbb{R}) = \mathbb{R}$.

We know that $f(\mathbb{R}) \subseteq \mathbb{R}$, so we must show that $f(\mathbb{R}) \supseteq \mathbb{R}$.

Let y be an arbitrary element in $\mathbb{R}$. We must show that $y \in f(\mathbb{R})$; that is, there exists an element x in the domain $\mathbb{R}$ such that

$$f(x) = y; \quad \text{that is,} \quad 2x - 5 = y.$$

Rearranging this equation, we obtain

$$x = \frac{y + 5}{2}.$$

This is in $\mathbb{R}$ and satisfies $f(x) = y$, as required. Thus $f(\mathbb{R}) \supseteq \mathbb{R}$.

Since $f(\mathbb{R}) \subseteq \mathbb{R}$ and $f(\mathbb{R}) \supseteq \mathbb{R}$, it follows that $f(\mathbb{R}) = \mathbb{R}$, so the image of f is indeed $\mathbb{R}$.

The codomain of f is also $\mathbb{R}$, so f is onto.

In this solution, we use $\supseteq$, rather than $\subseteq$, so that the image is always on the left and the codomain on the right.

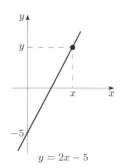

$y = 2x - 5$

(b) The sketch of the graph of f shown in the margin suggests that the image of f is $[0, \infty)$. We now prove algebraically that $f(\mathbb{R}) = [0, \infty)$.

Let x be an arbitrary element in the domain $\mathbb{R}$; then $f(x) = x^2 \geq 0$, so $f(\mathbb{R}) \subseteq [0, \infty)$.

We must show that $f(\mathbb{R}) \supseteq [0, \infty)$.

Let y be an arbitrary element in $[0, \infty)$. We must show that there exists an element x in the domain $\mathbb{R}$ such that

$$f(x) = y; \quad \text{that is,} \quad x^2 = y.$$

Now $x = \sqrt{y}$ is in $\mathbb{R}$ (since $y \geq 0$) and satisfies $f(x) = y$, as required. Thus $f(\mathbb{R}) \supseteq [0, \infty)$.

Since $f(\mathbb{R}) \subseteq [0, \infty)$ and $f(\mathbb{R}) \supseteq [0, \infty)$, it follows that $f(\mathbb{R}) = [0, \infty)$, so the image of f is $[0, \infty)$, as expected.

The interval $[0, \infty)$ is not the whole of the codomain, so f is not onto.

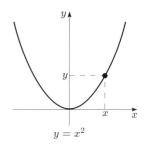

$y = x^2$

Alternatively, we could choose the real number $x = -\sqrt{y}$, which also satisfies $f(x) = y$.

(c) This function is a translation of the plane that shifts each point to the right by 1 unit and up by 2 units. This suggests that $f(\mathbb{R}^2) = \mathbb{R}^2$.

We know that $f(\mathbb{R}^2) \subseteq \mathbb{R}^2$, so we must show that $f(\mathbb{R}^2) \supseteq \mathbb{R}^2$.

Let (x', y') be an arbitrary element in the codomain $\mathbb{R}^2$. We must show that there exists an element (x, y) in the domain $\mathbb{R}^2$ such that

$$f(x, y) = (x', y'); \quad \text{that is,} \quad x' = x + 1, \quad y' = y + 2.$$

Rearranging these two equations, we obtain

$$x = x' - 1, \quad y = y' - 2.$$

With these values, $(x, y) \in \mathbb{R}^2$ and $f(x, y) = (x', y')$, as required. Thus $f(\mathbb{R}^2) \supseteq \mathbb{R}^2$.

Since $f(\mathbb{R}^2) \subseteq \mathbb{R}^2$ and $f(\mathbb{R}^2) \supseteq \mathbb{R}^2$, it follows that $f(\mathbb{R}^2) = \mathbb{R}^2$, so the image of f is $\mathbb{R}^2$, as expected.

The codomain of f is also $\mathbb{R}^2$, so f is onto.

(d) In Example 2.1, we showed that the image of this function is $\{0, 1, 2, 3, 4\}$. This is not the whole of the codomain, so f is not onto. ∎

Exercise 2.5 For each of the following functions, find its image and determine whether it is onto.

(a) $f : \mathbb{R} \longrightarrow \mathbb{R}$
    $x \longmapsto 1 + x^2$

(b) $f : \mathbb{R}^2 \longrightarrow \mathbb{R}^2$
    $(x, y) \longmapsto (x, -y)$

2.3 Inverse functions

Given a function

$$f : A \longrightarrow B$$
$$x \longmapsto f(x),$$

it is sometimes possible to define an *inverse function* that 'undoes' the effect of f by mapping each image element $f(x)$ back to the element x whose image it is. For example, a rotation can be 'undone' by a rotation in the opposite direction.

However, consider the function

$$f : A \longrightarrow A, \quad \text{where } A = \{0, 1, 2, 3, 4, 5, 6, 7, 8, 9\},$$
$$x \longmapsto \left[\tfrac{1}{2}x\right].$$

We know that $f(2) = f(3) = 1$, and so a function that 'undoes' the effect of f must map the number 1 to the number 2 *and* to the number 3, which is impossible. Thus, in this case, no inverse function exists. This function f is an example of a function that is *many-one*. A many-one function does not have an inverse function.

Definitions   A function $f : A \longrightarrow B$ is **one-one** if each element of $f(A)$ is the image of exactly one element of A; that is,

if $x_1, x_2 \in A$ and $f(x_1) = f(x_2)$,   then $x_1 = x_2$.

A function that is not one-one is **many-one**.

Some texts refer to a one-one function as an *injective* function.

We write $x_1, x_2 \in A$ as shorthand for $x_1 \in A$ and $x_2 \in A$.

Remark   Thus a function f is one-one if it maps distinct elements in the domain A to distinct elements in the image $f(A)$.

To prove that a function f is *not* one-one, it is sufficient to find a single *counter-example*—that is, a pair of *distinct* elements in the domain A with the *same* image in $f(A)$.

The term 'one-one' is often read as 'one to one'; similarly 'many-one' is often read as 'many to one'.

Exercise 2.6   Which of the following diagrams correspond(s) to a one-one function?

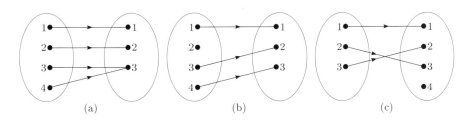

Example 2.3   Determine which of the following functions are one-one.

(a) $f : \mathbb{R} \longrightarrow \mathbb{R}$
  $x \longmapsto 2x - 5$

(b) $f : \mathbb{R} \longrightarrow \mathbb{R}$
  $x \longmapsto x^2$

(c) $f : \mathbb{R}^2 \longrightarrow \mathbb{R}^2$
  $(x, y) \longmapsto (x + 1, y + 2)$

Solution

(a) The graph suggests that f is one-one. We now prove this algebraically. Suppose that $f(x_1) = f(x_2)$; then

$$2x_1 - 5 = 2x_2 - 5,$$

so $2x_1 = 2x_2$, and hence $x_1 = x_2$.

Thus f is one-one.

(b) The graph suggests that f is not one-one. To show that f is not one-one, we just need to find two distinct points in the domain of f with the same image. For example,

$$f(2) = f(-2) = 4,$$

so f is not one-one.

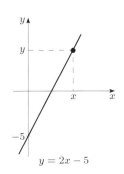

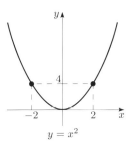

(c) This function is a translation of the plane, and so we expect it to be one-one. We now prove this algebraically.

Suppose that $f(x_1, y_1) = f(x_2, y_2)$; then

$$(x_1 + 1, y_1 + 2) = (x_2 + 1, y_2 + 2).$$

Thus

$$x_1 + 1 = x_2 + 1 \quad \text{and} \quad y_1 + 2 = y_2 + 2,$$

so $x_1 = x_2$ and $y_1 = y_2$.

Hence $(x_1, y_1) = (x_2, y_2)$, so f is one-one.   ∎

Exercise 2.7   Determine which of the following functions is one-one.

(a) $f : \mathbb{R} \longrightarrow \mathbb{R}$
$\quad\quad x \longmapsto 1 + x^2$

(b) $f : \mathbb{R}^2 \longrightarrow \mathbb{R}^2$
$\quad\quad (x, y) \longmapsto (x, -y)$

For a one-one function $f : A \longrightarrow B$, we have the situation illustrated in the margin. Each element y in $f(A)$ is the image of a unique element x in A, and so we can reverse the arrows to obtain the *inverse function* f^{-1}, with domain $f(A)$ and image A, which maps y back to x.

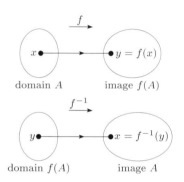

domain A image $f(A)$

domain $f(A)$ image A

Definition   Let $f : A \longrightarrow B$ be a one-one function. Then f has an **inverse function** $f^{-1} : f(A) \longrightarrow A$, with rule

$$f^{-1}(y) = x, \quad \text{where } y = f(x).$$

A function $f : A \longrightarrow B$ that is both one-one and onto has an inverse function $f^{-1} : B \longrightarrow A$. Such a function f is said to be a **one-one correspondence**, or a **bijection**, between the sets A and B.

Example 2.4   For each of the following functions, determine whether f has an inverse function f^{-1}; if it exists, find it.

(a) $f : \mathbb{R} \longrightarrow \mathbb{R}$
$\quad\quad x \longmapsto 2x - 5$

(b) $f : \mathbb{R} \longrightarrow \mathbb{R}$
$\quad\quad x \longmapsto x^2$

(c) $f : \mathbb{R}^2 \longrightarrow \mathbb{R}^2$
$\quad\quad (x, y) \longmapsto (x + 1, y + 2)$

(d) $f : A \longrightarrow A$ \quad where $A = \{0, 1, 2, 3, 4, 5, 6, 7, 8, 9\}$.
$\quad\quad x \longmapsto \left[\frac{1}{2}x\right]$

Solution

(a) In Example 2.3(a), we showed that f is one-one, so f has an inverse function.

In Example 2.2(a), we showed that the image of f is $\mathbb{R}$ and that, for each y in the image $\mathbb{R}$, we have

$$y = f\left(\frac{y + 5}{2}\right).$$

So f^{-1} is the function

$$f^{-1} : \mathbb{R} \longrightarrow \mathbb{R}$$
$$y \longmapsto \frac{y + 5}{2}.$$

This definition can be expressed in terms of x as

$$f^{-1} : \mathbb{R} \longrightarrow \mathbb{R}$$
$$x \longmapsto \frac{x + 5}{2}.$$

It does not matter whether the definition of f^{-1} is expressed in terms of x or y, but it is more usual to use x in the definition of a real function.

(b) In Example 2.3(b), we showed that f is not one-one, so f does not have an inverse function.

(c) In Example 2.3(c), we showed that f is one-one, so f has an inverse function.

In Example 2.2(c), we showed that the image of f is $\mathbb{R}^2$ and that, for each (x', y') in the image $\mathbb{R}^2$, we have

$$(x', y') = f(x' - 1, y' - 2).$$

So f^{-1} is the function

$$f^{-1} : \mathbb{R}^2 \longrightarrow \mathbb{R}^2$$
$$(x', y') \longmapsto (x' - 1, y' - 2).$$

Geometrically, f is the translation of the plane that shifts each point to the right by 1 unit and up by 2 units. Since f^{-1} undoes the effect of f, the inverse f^{-1} is the translation that shifts each point to the left by 1 unit and down by 2 units.

This definition can be expressed in terms of x and y as

$$f^{-1} : \mathbb{R}^2 \longrightarrow \mathbb{R}^2$$
$$(x, y) \longmapsto (x - 1, y - 2).$$

(d) At the beginning of this subsection, we showed that f is not one-one, so f does not have an inverse function. ■

Exercise 2.8   For each of the following functions, determine whether f has an inverse function f^{-1}; if it exists, find f^{-1}.

(a) $f : \mathbb{R} \longrightarrow \mathbb{R}$
     $x \longmapsto 1 + x^2$

(b) $f : \mathbb{R}^2 \longrightarrow \mathbb{R}^2$
     $(x, y) \longmapsto (x, -y)$

(c) $f : \mathbb{R} \longrightarrow \mathbb{R}$
     $x \longmapsto 8x + 3$

Hint: For parts (a) and (b), use your answers to Exercises 2.5 and 2.7.

Restrictions

When given a function $f : A \longrightarrow B$, it is often convenient to restrict attention to the behaviour of f on some subset C of A. For example, consider the function

$$f : \mathbb{R} \longrightarrow \mathbb{R}$$
$$x \longmapsto x^2.$$

This function is not one-one and so does not have an inverse function. However, if the domain of f is replaced by the set $C = [0, \infty)$, then we obtain a related function

$$g : C \longrightarrow \mathbb{R}$$
$$x \longmapsto x^2.$$

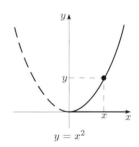

$y = x^2$

The rule is the same as for f, but the domain is 'restricted' to produce a new function g that is one-one and so has an inverse.

The function g is an example of a *restriction* of f in the sense that $g(x) = f(x)$ for all x in the domain of g.

More generally, we define a restriction as follows.

Definition   Let $f : A \longrightarrow B$ and let C be a subset of the domain A. Then the function $g : C \longrightarrow B$ defined by

$$g(x) = f(x), \quad \text{for } x \in C,$$

is the **restriction** of f to C.

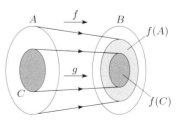

g is the restriction of f to C

Exercise 2.9   Let f be the function

$$f : \mathbb{R} \longrightarrow \mathbb{R}$$
$$x \longmapsto |x|.$$

Write down a restriction of f that is one-one.

2.4 Composite functions

Earlier, we described how a function may be regarded as a machine that processes elements in the domain to produce elements in the codomain. Now suppose that two such machines are linked together, so that the elements emerging from the first machine are fed into the second machine for further processing. The overall effect is to create a new 'composite' machine that corresponds to a so-called *composite* function.

Consider the real functions

$$f : \mathbb{R} \longrightarrow \mathbb{R} \qquad \text{and} \qquad g : \mathbb{R} \longrightarrow \mathbb{R}$$
$$x \longmapsto x^2 \qquad\qquad\qquad x \longmapsto 2x - 5.$$

When the machines for f and g are linked together so that objects are first processed by f and then by g, we obtain the 'composite' machine illustrated by the dark blue box in the diagram below.

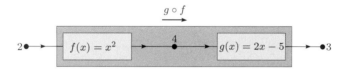

For example, when 2 is fed into the machine, it is first squared by f to produce the number 4, and then 4 is processed by g to give the number $(2 \times 4) - 5 = 3$.

Similarly, when an arbitrary real number x is fed into the machine, it is first processed by f to give the real number x^2. Since the domain of g is the whole of $\mathbb{R}$, the number x^2 can then be processed by g to give $2x^2 - 5$. Thus, overall, the composite machine corresponds to a function, denoted by $g \circ f$, whose rule is

$$(g \circ f)(x) = g(f(x)) = 2x^2 - 5$$

Remember that $g \circ f$ means f first, then g.

and whose domain is $\mathbb{R}$.

In general, if $f : A \longrightarrow B$ and $g : B \longrightarrow C$, then we can form the *composite function*

$$g \circ f : A \longrightarrow C$$
$$x \longmapsto g(f(x)).$$

Here the domain of the function $g : B \longrightarrow C$ is the same as the codomain of the function $f : A \longrightarrow B$.

Exercise 2.10   Let f and g be the functions

$$f : \mathbb{R} \longrightarrow \mathbb{R} \qquad \text{and} \qquad g : \mathbb{R} \longrightarrow \mathbb{R}$$
$$x \longmapsto -x \qquad\qquad\qquad x \longmapsto 3x + 1.$$

Determine the composite functions

(a) $g \circ f$,   (b) $f \circ g$.

The composite functions $g \circ f$ and $f \circ g$ are not equal in general, as you saw in the above exercise.

Composite functions have many uses in mathematics. In geometry, they are frequently used to examine the effect of one transformation of the plane followed by another.

Suppose, for example, that f and g are the reflections of the plane in the x-axis and y-axis respectively:

$$f : \mathbb{R}^2 \longrightarrow \mathbb{R}^2 \qquad \text{and} \qquad g : \mathbb{R}^2 \longrightarrow \mathbb{R}^2$$
$$(x, y) \longmapsto (x, -y) \qquad\qquad (x, y) \longmapsto (-x, y).$$

The composite function $g \circ f$ describes the overall effect of first reflecting in the x-axis (changing the sign of y) and then reflecting in the y-axis (changing the sign of x).

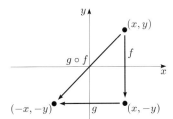

The rule of $g \circ f$ is

$$(g \circ f)(x, y) = g(f(x, y)) = g(x, -y)$$
$$= (-x, -y).$$

Thus $g \circ f$ is the function

$$g \circ f : \mathbb{R}^2 \longrightarrow \mathbb{R}^2$$
$$(x, y) \longmapsto (-x, -y),$$

which rotates the plane through π about the origin.

For example, a square is transformed as follows.

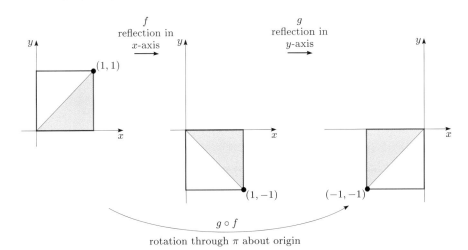

Exercise 2.11   Determine the composite function $f \circ g$ of the following transformations of the plane:

$$f : \mathbb{R}^2 \longrightarrow \mathbb{R}^2 \qquad \text{and} \qquad g : \mathbb{R}^2 \longrightarrow \mathbb{R}^2$$
$$(x, y) \longmapsto (x, -y) \qquad\qquad (x, y) \longmapsto (-x, y).$$

So far, we have considered the composite function $g \circ f$ only when the domain of the function $g : B \longrightarrow C$ is the same as the codomain of the function $f : A \longrightarrow B$. We can, however, form the composite function $g \circ f$ when g and f are *any* two functions.

For example, consider the functions

$$f : \mathbb{R} \longrightarrow \mathbb{R} \quad \text{and} \quad g : \mathbb{R} - \{1\} \longrightarrow \mathbb{R}$$
$$x \longmapsto x^2 \qquad \qquad x \longmapsto \frac{1}{x-1}.$$

Here the domain of g is not equal to the codomain of f, but we can still consider the composite function $g \circ f$, with the rule

$$(g \circ f)(x) = g(f(x)) = g(x^2) = \frac{1}{x^2 - 1}.$$

In this case, the domain of $g \circ f$ cannot be $\mathbb{R}$ (the domain of f) since 1 and -1 are both mapped by f to the number 1, which is not in the domain of g; this means that no further processing is possible.

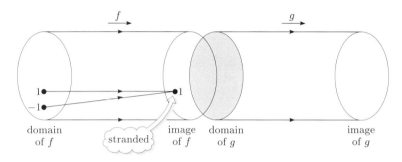

To overcome this difficulty, we take the domain of $g \circ f$ to be the difference $\mathbb{R} - \{1, -1\}$. So the composite function $g \circ f$ is

$$g \circ f : \mathbb{R} - \{1, -1\} \longrightarrow \mathbb{R}$$
$$x \longmapsto \frac{1}{x^2 - 1}.$$

The general situation is illustrated below. Given any two functions $f : A \longrightarrow B$ and $g : C \longrightarrow D$, the rule of the composite function $g \circ f$ is

$$(g \circ f)(x) = g(f(x)).$$

The domain of $g \circ f$ consists of all those elements x in A for which $f(x)$ lies in C (the domain of g). The codomain of $g \circ f$ is defined to be D (the codomain of g).

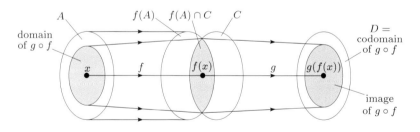

Definition   Let $f : A \longrightarrow B$ and $g : C \longrightarrow D$ be any two functions; then the **composite function** $g \circ f$ has

    domain $\{x \in A : f(x) \in C\}$,

    codomain D,

    rule $(g \circ f)(x) = g(f(x))$.

This definition allows us to consider the composite of *any* two functions, although in some cases the domain may turn out to be the empty set $\varnothing$. Some authors insist upon $f(A) \subseteq C$ as a condition for $g \circ f$ to exist.

In the example on page 32, the domain of $g \circ f$ is just the set of values for which the rule of $g \circ f$ is defined. This is not the case in the following exercise.

Exercise 2.12 Determine the composite function $g \circ f$ for the following functions f and g:

$$f : [-1, 1] \longrightarrow \mathbb{R} \qquad g : \mathbb{R} - \{-2\} \longrightarrow \mathbb{R}$$
$$x \longmapsto 3x + 1 \quad \text{and} \quad x \longmapsto \frac{3}{x + 2}.$$

Composites and inverses

Suppose that $f : A \longrightarrow B$ is a one-one and onto function. Then f has an inverse function $f^{-1} : B \longrightarrow A$. We can therefore consider the effect that the composite function $f^{-1} \circ f : A \longrightarrow A$ has on an arbitrary element x in A. First, f maps x to an element $y = f(x)$ in $f(A)$. Then f^{-1} 'undoes' the effect of f and maps y back to x. Overall, the effect of $f^{-1} \circ f$ is to leave x fixed: that is, $(f^{-1} \circ f)(x) = x$. Since x is an arbitrary element of A, it follows that $f^{-1} \circ f$ fixes all the elements of A. In other words, $f^{-1} \circ f = i_A$.

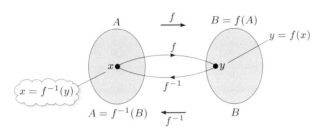

Similar arguments can be used to show that $f \circ f^{-1} = i_B$. So, if $f : A \longrightarrow B$ has an inverse function $f^{-1} : B \longrightarrow A$, then

$$f^{-1} \circ f = i_A \quad \text{and} \quad f \circ f^{-1} = i_B.$$

The converse of this statement is also true: if a function $g : B \longrightarrow A$ satisfies

$$g \circ f = i_A \quad \text{and} \quad f \circ g = i_B,$$

then g is the inverse function of f. We shall prove this after Exercise 2.13. It leads to the following strategy.

Strategy 2.1 To show that the function $g : B \longrightarrow A$ is the inverse function of the function $f : A \longrightarrow B$.

1. Show that $f(g(x)) = x$ for each $x \in B$; that is, $f \circ g = i_B$.

2. Show that $g(f(x)) = x$ for each $x \in A$; that is, $g \circ f = i_A$.

In practice, we can sometimes use Strategy 2.1 as an alternative way of *finding* an inverse function. We make an inspired guess at the function, and use Strategy 2.1 to check that our guess is correct.

Example 2.5 Find the inverse of the function

$$g : \mathbb{R} \longrightarrow \mathbb{R}$$
$$x \longmapsto \tfrac{1}{2}x.$$

Solution We guess that the inverse function is

$$f : \mathbb{R} \longrightarrow \mathbb{R}$$
$$x \longmapsto 2x.$$

We use Strategy 2.1 to check that our guess is correct.

1. For each $x \in \mathbb{R}$, we have
$$f(g(x)) = f(\tfrac{1}{2}x) = 2 \times \tfrac{1}{2}x = x;$$
that is, $f \circ g = i_{\mathbb{R}}$.

2. For each $x \in \mathbb{R}$, we have
$$g(f(x)) = g(2x) = \tfrac{1}{2} \times 2x = x;$$
that is, $g \circ f = i_{\mathbb{R}}$.

Since $f \circ g = i_{\mathbb{R}}$ and $g \circ f = i_{\mathbb{R}}$, it follows that g is the inverse function of f. ∎

Exercise 2.13   Use Strategy 2.1 to show that

$$g : \mathbb{R} \longrightarrow \mathbb{R}$$
$$x \longmapsto x - 3$$

is the inverse function of

$$f : \mathbb{R} \longrightarrow \mathbb{R}$$
$$x \longmapsto x + 3.$$

We end this section by proving, as promised, that if the functions $f : A \longrightarrow B$ and $g : B \longrightarrow A$ satisfy

$$g \circ f = i_A \quad \text{and} \quad f \circ g = i_B,$$

then g is the inverse function of f. That is, we have to show that if the two steps of Strategy 2.1 hold, then f has an inverse function, and the inverse function is equal to g. Suppose that the two steps of Strategy 2.1 hold.

First we show that f is one-one. Suppose that $f(x_1) = f(x_2)$; then

$$g(f(x_1)) = g(f(x_2)),$$

so, by step 2, $x_1 = x_2$. Thus f is one-one and so it has an inverse function f^{-1}.

Now we find the image of f. We know that the image of f is a subset of its codomain B; we shall show that it is equal to B by showing that every element y of B is the image under f of some element in A. Suppose that $y \in B$. Then, by step 1,

$$f(g(y)) = y;$$

that is, y is the image under f of the element $g(y)$, as required. Thus the image of f is B (that is, f is onto), and so f^{-1} has domain B.

We now know that each of the functions f^{-1} and g has domain B and codomain A. To show that they are equal, it remains to show that $g(y) = f^{-1}(y)$ for each element y of B. Let y be an arbitrary element of B. Then $y = f(x)$ for some element x of A. So

$$f^{-1}(y) = x,$$

and, by step 2,

$$g(y) = g(f(x)) = x.$$

Hence f^{-1} and g are indeed equal functions.

Further exercises

Exercise 2.14   For each of the following transformations $f : \mathbb{R}^2 \longrightarrow \mathbb{R}^2$, state whether f is a translation, reflection or rotation of the plane.

(a) $f(x, y) = (y, -x)$ (b) $f(x, y) = (x - 2, y + 1)$

Exercise 2.15   Draw a diagram showing the image of T, the triangle with vertices at $(0, 0)$, $(1, 0)$ and $(1, 1)$, under each of the functions f of Exercise 2.14.

Exercise 2.16   For each of the following functions, find its image and determine whether it is onto.

(a) $f : \mathbb{R}^2 \longrightarrow \mathbb{R}^2$ (b) $f : \mathbb{R} \longrightarrow \mathbb{R}$
$\quad (x, y) \longmapsto (-y, x)$ $\quad x \longmapsto 7 - 3x$

(c) $f : \mathbb{R} \longrightarrow \mathbb{R}$ (d) $f : [0, 1] \longrightarrow \mathbb{R}$
$\quad x \longmapsto x^2 - 4x + 3$ $\quad x \longmapsto 2x + 3$

Exercise 2.17   Determine which of the functions in Exercise 2.16 are one-one.

Exercise 2.18   Determine which of the functions in Exercise 2.16 has an inverse, and find the inverse f^{-1} for each one which does.

Exercise 2.19   Determine the composite $f \circ g$ for each of the following pairs of functions f and g.

(a) $f : \mathbb{R} \longrightarrow \mathbb{R}$ and $g : \mathbb{R} - \{2, -2\} \longrightarrow \mathbb{R}$
$\quad x \longmapsto 7 - 3x$ $\quad\quad\quad x \longmapsto \dfrac{1}{x^2 - 4}.$

(b) $f : \mathbb{R}^2 \longrightarrow \mathbb{R}^2$ and $g : \mathbb{R}^2 \longrightarrow \mathbb{R}^2$
$\quad (x, y) \longmapsto (-y, x)$ $\quad (x, y) \longmapsto (y, x).$

3   The language of proof

After working through this section, you should be able to:

(a) understand what is asserted by various types of mathematical statements, in particular *implications* and *equivalences*;

(b) produce simple proofs of various types, including *direct proof, proof by induction, proof by contradiction* and *proof by contraposition*;

(c) read and understand the logic of more complex proofs;

(d) disprove a simple false implication by providing a *counter-example*.

You will have seen many examples of mathematical statements, theorems and proofs during your study of mathematics. In this section we examine these concepts more closely. This should help you to become more adept at reading and understanding mathematics, and should make you more familiar with the structures of various different types of mathematical proof. It should also help you to express your own mathematical thoughts and ideas more clearly.

3.1 Statements and negations

The building blocks of mathematical theorems and proofs are assertions called **statements**, also known as *propositions*. In mathematics, a statement is an assertion that is either true or false, though we may not know which. The following are examples of statements.

1.   The equation $2x - 3 = 0$ has solution $x = \frac{3}{2}$.

2. $1 + 1 = 3$.

3. $1 + 3 + 5 + \cdots + (2n - 1) = n^2$ for each positive integer n.

4.   There is a real number x such that $\cos x = x$.

5.   Every even integer greater than 2 is the sum of two prime numbers.

6. x is greater than 0.

In the above list, Statement 1 is true, and Statement 2 is false. Statements 3 and 4 are in fact both true, although this is probably not immediately obvious to you in either case. At the time of writing this unit, it is not known whether Statement 5 is true or false.

Statement 6 is a little different from the others, since whether it is true or false depends on the value of the variable x. A statement, such as this one, that is either true or false depending on the value of one or more variables, is called a *variable proposition*. When considering a variable proposition, we must have in mind a suitable set of values from which the possible values of the variable are taken. For example, the set associated with Statement 6 might be $\mathbb{R}$, since for each real number x the assertion is either true or false. A variable proposition with several variables may have several such associated sets.

Often the set or sets associated with a variable are clear from the context and so we do not state them explicitly. In particular, unless it is stated otherwise, it is conventional to assume that if the variable is x or y, then the associated set is $\mathbb{R}$, whereas if the variable is n or m, then the associated set is is $\mathbb{Z}$ or $\mathbb{N}$, depending on the context. We follow this convention in this section.

An example of an assertion that is not a mathematical statement is '$\{1, 2\}$ is greater than 0', which is meaningless and therefore neither true nor false. Other examples are 'π is interesting' and '1000 is a large number', which are not precise enough to be either true or false.

Statements can be combined in various ways to give more complicated statements. For example, the statement

> x is greater than 0 and x is an integer

is true if *both* of the statements 'x is greater than 0' and 'x is an integer' are true, and false otherwise. Thus the combined statement is true if $x = 4$, for example, but false if $x = 3.5$. Similarly, the statement

> x is greater than 0 or x is an integer

is true if *at least one* of the statements 'x is greater than 0' and 'x is an integer' is true, and false otherwise. Thus this combined statement is true if $x = 4$, $x = 3.5$ or $x = -4$, for example, but false if $x = -3.5$.

Every statement has a related statement, called its **negation**, which is true when the original statement is false, and false when the original statement is true. The negation of a statement P can usually be written as 'it is not the case that P', but there are often better, more concise ways to express it. Thus, for example, the negation of the statement 'x is greater than 0' can be written as 'it is not the case that x is greater than 0', but is

We shall prove that Statement 3 is true later in this section. You can check that Statement 4 is true by noting that the graphs of $y = \cos x$ and $y = x$ intersect; a rigorous proof can be obtained by using the *Intermediate Value Theorem*, which is given later in the course. Statement 5 is known as *Goldbach's conjecture*; mathematicians have been trying to prove it since 1742.

The word 'or' is used in its inclusive sense in mathematical statements.

better expressed as 'x is not greater than 0' or even '$x \leq 0$'. The process of finding the negation of a statement is called *negating* the statement. Here are some more examples.

Example 3.1   Express concisely the negation of each of the following statements.

(a) There is a real number x such that $\cos x = x$.

(b) Both x and y are integers.

Solution

(a) The negation is 'it is not the case that there is an real number x such that $\cos x = x$'; that is, 'there is no real number x such that $\cos x = x$'.

(b) The negation is 'it is not the case that both x and y are integers'; that is, 'at least one of x and y is not an integer'.   ■

Another way of expressing this negation is 'for all real numbers x, $\cos x \neq x$'.

Exercise 3.1   Express concisely the negation of each of the following statements.

(a) $x = \frac{3}{5}$ is a solution of the equation $3x + 5 = 0$.

(b) π is less than 5.

(c) There is an integer that is divisible by 3 but not by 6.

(d) Every real number x satisfies the inequality $x^2 \geq 0$.

(e) The integers m and n are both odd.

(f) At least one of the integers m and n is odd.

A **theorem** is simply a mathematical statement that is true. However, we usually reserve the word for a statement that is considered to be of some importance, and whose truth is not immediately obvious, but instead has to be proved. A **lemma** is a 'less important' theorem that is useful when proving other theorems. A **corollary** is a theorem that follows from another theorem by a short additional argument. Theorems are sometimes called *results*.

3.2 Implications and equivalences

Many mathematical statements are of the form 'if something, then something else', for example:

   if $x > 2$, then $x^2 > 4$.

This type of statement is called an **implication**. An implication is made up from two smaller statements, which in the example above are '$x > 2$' and '$x^2 > 4$', and can be expressed by combining these statements using the words 'if' and 'then'. In an implication 'if P, then Q', the statement P is called the **hypothesis** of the implication, and the statement Q is called the **conclusion**. It is important to be clear about exactly what an implication asserts. The above statement asserts only that if you know that $x > 2$, then you can be sure that $x^2 > 4$. It does not assert anything about the truth or falsity of '$x^2 > 4$' when x is not greater than 2. In general, the implication 'if P, then Q' asserts that if P is true, then Q is also true; it does not assert anything about the truth or falsity of Q when P is false.

If the hypothesis P of an implication consists of several smaller statements, combined using 'and'—for example, the implication might be expressed in the form 'if P_1, P_2 and P_3, then Q'—then it is common to consider each of the smaller statements as a separate hypothesis, and to say that the implication has several *hypotheses*. Similarly, an implication can have several conclusions.

If x is a real variable, then the statement

if $x > 2$, then $x^2 > 4$

is true because for every real number x for which '$x > 2$' is true, '$x^2 > 4$' is true also. Strictly speaking, this statement should be expressed as

for all $x \in \mathbb{R}$, if $x > 2$, then $x^2 > 4$.

However, it is conventional to omit the initial 'for all $x \in \mathbb{R}$', and interpret the statement as if it were there. In general, throughout this course, and throughout almost any mathematical text that you will read, a statement of the form 'if P, then Q' in which P and/or Q are variable propositions is similarly interpreted as applying to all values of the variables in the statements P and Q.

An implication does not have to be expressed using the words 'if' and 'then'—there are many other ways to convey the same meaning. The left-hand side of the table below lists some ways of expressing the implication 'if P, then Q'. The right-hand side gives similar examples, but for the particular implication 'if $x > 2$, then $x^2 > 4$'.

Ways of writing 'if P, then Q'	Ways of writing 'if $x > 2$, then $x^2 > 4$'
P implies Q	$x > 2$ implies $x^2 > 4$
$P \Rightarrow Q$	$x > 2 \Rightarrow x^2 > 4$
Q whenever P	$x^2 > 4$ whenever $x > 2$
	(or: $x^2 > 4$, for all $x > 2$)
Q follows from P	$x^2 > 4$ follows from $x > 2$
P is sufficient for Q	$x > 2$ is sufficient for $x^2 > 4$
Q is necessary for P	$x^2 > 4$ is necessary for $x > 2$
P only if Q	$x > 2$ only if $x^2 > 4$

The symbol $\Rightarrow$ is read as 'implies'.

The form 'P only if Q' may seem strange at first; it asserts that the only circumstance in which P can be true is if Q is also true—that is, P implies Q.

Exercise 3.2   Rewrite each of the following statements in the form 'if P, then Q'. In each case, state whether you think the implication is true. You are not asked to justify your answers.

(a) $x^2 - 2x + 1 = 0 \Rightarrow (x-1)^2 = 0$.

(b) Whenever n is odd, so is n^3.

(c) Every integer that is divisible by 3 is also divisible by 6.

(d) $x > 2$ only if $x > 4$.

You will see how to prove or disprove statements like those in parts (b) and (c) formally later in this section. Whether the statement in part (a) is true or false may be established by algebraic manipulation.

The **converse** of the implication 'if P, then Q' is the implication 'if Q, then P'. For example, the converse of the implication

if $x > 2$, then $x^2 > 4$

is

if $x^2 > 4$, then $x > 2$.

In this example, the original implication is true, and its converse is false. It is also possible for an implication and its converse to be both true, or both false. In other words, knowledge of whether an implication is true or false tells you *nothing at all* about whether its converse is true or false. You should remember this important fact whenever you read or write implications.

To see that the converse is false, consider, for example, $x = -3$.

To help you remember facts like this about statements, you may find it helpful to consider non-mathematical examples. For example, consider the implication 'if Rosie is a sheep, then Rosie is less than two metres tall.' This implication is true, but its converse, 'if Rosie is less than two metres tall, then Rosie is a sheep', certainly is not!

> **Exercise 3.3** Write down the converse of each of the following statements about integers m and n. In each case, state whether you think the statement is true and whether you think the converse is true. You are not asked to justify your answers at this stage.
>
> (a) If m and n are both odd, then $m + n$ is even.
>
> (b) If one of the pair m, n is even and the other is odd, then $m + n$ is odd.

The statement 'if P, then Q, and if Q, then P', which asserts that the implication 'if P, then Q' and its converse are *both* true, is usually expressed more concisely as 'P if and only if Q'. Here are two examples.

1. n is odd if and only if n^2 is odd.
2. $x > 2$ if and only if $x^2 > 4$.

'P if Q' means '$Q \Rightarrow P$', and 'P only if Q' means '$P \Rightarrow Q$'.

Statements like these are called **equivalences**. Equivalence 1 above is true, because both implications are true, whereas equivalence 2 is false, because the implication 'if $x^2 > 4$, then $x > 2$' is false. As with implications, there are many different ways to express equivalences. The table below lists some ways in which this can be done.

Ways of writing 'P if and only if Q'	Ways of writing 'n is odd if and only if n^2 is odd'
$P \Leftrightarrow Q$	n is odd $\Leftrightarrow$ n^2 is odd
P is **equivalent** to Q	n is odd is equivalent to n^2 is odd
P is necessary and sufficient for Q	n is odd is necessary and sufficient for n^2 to be odd

The symbol $\Leftrightarrow$ is usually read as 'if and only if', or sometimes as 'is equivalent to'.

> **Exercise 3.4** For each of the following equivalences about integers, write down the two implications that it asserts, state whether you think each is true, and hence state whether you think the equivalence is true. You are not asked to justify your answers at this stage.
>
> (a) The product mn is odd if and only if both m and n are odd.
>
> (b) The product mn is even if and only if both m and n are even.

Although a mathematical statement should normally be interpreted as meaning precisely what it says—no more and no less, there is one common exception to this rule. When giving a definition, we usually write 'if' when we really mean 'if and only if'. For example, we write

> a function $f : A \longrightarrow B$ is onto if $f(A) = B$.

3.3 Direct proof

A *proof* of a mathematical statement is a logical argument that establishes that the statement is true. Here is a simple example.

Example 3.2   Prove the following statement:

> If n is an odd number between 0 and 10, then n^2 is also odd.

Solution   The odd numbers between 0 and 10 are 1, 3, 5, 7, and 9. The squares of these numbers are 1, 9, 25, 49 and 81, respectively, and these are all odd.   ∎

In the above example, there were only a small number of possibilities to consider, and so it was easy to prove the statement by considering each one in turn. This method of proof is known as *proof by exhaustion*, because we exhaust all possibilities. In contrast, it is not possible to prove the statement 'If n is an odd number, then n^2 is also odd' using proof by exhaustion, because there are infinitely many possibilities to consider. Most mathematical statements that you will come across cannot be proved by exhaustion, because there are too many possibilities to consider—usually infinitely many. Instead we must supply a general proof.

Suppose that we wish to prove that the implication $P \Rightarrow Q$ is true. We have to prove that whenever the statement P is true, the statement Q is also true. Often the best way to do this is to start out by *assuming* that P is true, and proceed as follows. If we know that the statement

$$P \Rightarrow P_1$$

is true for some statement P_1, then we can deduce that P_1 is also true. Similarly, if we know that the statement

$$P_1 \Rightarrow P_2$$

is true for some statement P_2, then we can deduce that P_2 is also true. In this way we can build up a sequence of statements

$$P, P_1, P_2, \ldots,$$

each of which we know to be true under the assumption that P is true. The aim is to build up such a sequence

$$P, P_1, P_2, \ldots, P_n, Q,$$

which leads to Q. If this can be achieved, then we have a proof of the implication $P \Rightarrow Q$. Here is an example.

Example 3.3   Prove that if n is odd, then n^2 is odd.

Solution   Let n be an odd integer. Then

$$n = 2k + 1 \text{ for some integer } k.$$

Hence

$$n^2 = (2k+1)^2 = (2k)^2 + 2(2k) + 1 = 2(2k^2 + 2k) + 1.$$

This shows that n^2 is an odd integer.   ∎

We see that n^2 is odd because we have shown that n^2 is equal to 2 times some integer plus 1.

In the above proof, statement P is 'n is odd', and we start by assuming that this is true. Statement P_1 is '$n = 2k + 1$ for some integer k', and so on. We use words like 'then' and 'hence' to indicate that one statement follows from another.

The string of equalities
$$n^2 = \cdots = 2(2k^2 + 2k) + 1$$
in the proof in Example 3.3 can be regarded either as a sequence of three statements, namely
$$n^2 = (2k+1)^2,$$
$$n^2 = (2k)^2 + 2(2k) + 1,$$
$$n^2 = 2(2k^2 + 2k) + 1,$$
or as a single statement asserting the equality of all four expressions.

Many of the true statements about odd and even integers that appeared in the exercises in the last subsection can be proved using ideas similar to those of the proof in Example 3.3; that is, we write an odd integer as $2 \times$ some integer $+ 1$, and an even integer as $2 \times$ some integer. (Similarly, we can often prove statements about multiples of 3 by writing each such number as $3 \times$ some integer, and so on.) Here is another example.

Example 3.4   Prove that the sum of two odd integers is even.

Solution   Let x and y be odd integers. Then

$x = 2k + 1$ and $y = 2l + 1$ for some integers k and l.

Hence

$x + y = (2k + 1) + (2l + 1) = 2k + 2l + 2 = 2(k + l + 1).$

This shows that $x + y$ is an even integer.   ∎

It is important to choose different symbols k and l here. We certainly cannot deduce from the first statement that $x = 2k + 1$ and $y = 2k + 1$ for some integer k; that would be the case only if x and y were equal!

We have seen that a sequence $P, P_1, P_2, \ldots, P_n, Q$ of statements forms a proof of the implication $P \Rightarrow Q$ provided that each statement is shown to be true under the assumption that P is true. In Examples 3.3 and 3.4 each statement in the sequence was deduced from the statement immediately before, but the sequence can also include statements that are deduced from one or more statements further back in the sequence, and statements that we know to be true from our previous mathematical knowledge. This is illustrated by the next example.

A fact that you may already know which will be useful in this example, and also later in this section, is that every integer greater than 1 has a unique expression as a product of primes. For example, $6468 = 2 \times 2 \times 3 \times 7 \times 7 \times 11$, and this is the only way to express 6468 as a product of primes (except of course that we can change the order of the primes in the expression). This fact is known as the *Fundamental Theorem of Arithmetic*.

Recall that a *prime number* is an integer n, greater than 1, whose only positive factors are 1 and n.

It is certainly not obvious that the Fundamental Theorem of Arithmetic is true! However, a proof is outside the scope of this unit.

Example 3.5   Prove that for every integer n, the number $n^3 + 3n^2 + 2n$ is divisible by 6.

Solution   Let n be an integer. Now

$n^3 + 3n^2 + 2n = n(n^2 + 3n + 2) = n(n + 1)(n + 2).$

Thus $n^3 + 3n^2 + 2n$ is the product of three consecutive integers. We know that out of any two consecutive integers, one must be divisible by 2, and out of any three consecutive integers, one must be divisible by 3. It follows that the three factors n, $n + 1$ and $n + 2$ include one that is divisible by 2, and one that is divisible by 3 (possibly the same one). Hence both the primes 2 and 3 are factors of $n^3 + 3n^2 + 2n$. Hence (by the Fundamental Theorem of Arithmetic) $n^3 + 3n^2 + 2n$ can be expressed as $2 \times 3 \times r$ for some integer r, and so it is divisible by $6 = 2 \times 3$.   ∎

In this course you are expected to be able to produce only simple proofs yourself. However, you should also be able to read through more complex proofs like some of those later in the course, and understand why they prove the statements that they claim to prove.

The next exercise gives you practice in the techniques that you have seen in this subsection.

Exercise 3.5   Prove each of the following implications.

(a) If n is an even integer, then n^2 is even.

(b) If m and n are multiples of k, then so is $m + n$.

(c) If one of the pair m, n is odd and the other is even, then $m + n$ is odd.

(d) If n is a positive integer, then $n^2 + n$ is even.

If a proof of an implication is particularly simple, and each statement in the sequence follows directly from the one immediately before, then we sometimes present the proof by writing the sequence of statements in the form

$$P \Rightarrow P_1 \Rightarrow P_2 \Rightarrow P_3 \Rightarrow \cdots \Rightarrow P_n \Rightarrow Q.$$

It is conventional to write this to indicate that each of the statements $P \Rightarrow P_1$, $P_1 \Rightarrow P_2$, ..., $P_n \Rightarrow Q$ is true.

This is particularly appropriate for proofs that depend mostly on algebraic manipulation. Here is an example.

Example 3.6   Prove that if $x(x-2) = 3$, then $x = -1$ or $x = 3$.

Solution

$$\begin{aligned} x(x-2) = 3 &\Rightarrow x^2 - 2x - 3 = 0 \\ &\Rightarrow (x+1)(x-3) = 0 \\ &\Rightarrow x+1 = 0 \text{ or } x - 3 = 0 \\ &\Rightarrow x = -1 \text{ or } x = 3. \quad \blacksquare \end{aligned}$$

By proving the implication in Example 3.6, we showed that -1 and 3 are the only possibilities for solutions of the equation $x(x-2) = 3$. We did not show that -1 and 3 actually *are* solutions, since for that it is necessary to prove also that if $x = -1$ or $x = 3$, then $x(x-2) = 3$, that is, the *converse* of the given implication. Thus strictly we have not solved the equation! Whenever we solve an equation, an implication and its converse must both be proved; in other words, we need to prove an equivalence. We do this for the equation in Example 3.6 shortly.

See Example 3.7.

First we discuss how to prove equivalences in general. Since an equivalence asserts that two implications are true, the best way to prove it is usually to tackle each implication separately. However, if a simple proof of one of the implications can be found, in which each statement follows from the one before, then it is sometimes possible to 'reverse all the arrows' to obtain a proof of the converse implication. That is, if you have found a proof of the form

$$P \Rightarrow P_1 \Rightarrow P_2 \Rightarrow P_3 \Rightarrow \cdots \Rightarrow P_n \Rightarrow Q,$$

Recall that the equivalence 'P if and only if Q' asserts that both the implication '$P \Rightarrow Q$' ('P only if Q') and its converse '$Q \Rightarrow P$' ('P if Q') are true.

then you *may* find that also each of the following implications is true:

$$Q \Rightarrow P_n \Rightarrow \cdots \Rightarrow P_3 \Rightarrow P_2 \Rightarrow P_1 \Rightarrow P.$$

In this case you may be able to present the proofs of both implications at once, by writing

$$P \Leftrightarrow P_1 \Leftrightarrow P_2 \Leftrightarrow P_3 \Leftrightarrow \cdots \Leftrightarrow P_n \Leftrightarrow Q.$$

As with implications, this is particularly appropriate for proofs that depend mostly on algebraic manipulation. The next example gives a proof of this type showing that the implication in Example 3.6 and its converse are both true.

Example 3.7   Prove that $x(x-2) = 3$ if and only if $x = -1$ or $x = 3$.

Solution

$$\begin{aligned} x(x-2) = 3 &\Leftrightarrow x^2 - 2x - 3 = 0 \\ &\Leftrightarrow (x+1)(x-3) = 0 \\ &\Leftrightarrow x+1 = 0 \text{ or } x - 3 = 0 \\ &\Leftrightarrow x = -1 \text{ or } x = 3. \quad \blacksquare \end{aligned}$$

Remember that the symbols $\Leftrightarrow$ and $\Rightarrow$ are used to link *statements*, not *expressions*. It is meaningless to write, for example, $x^2 - 2x - 3 \Leftrightarrow (x+1)(x-3)$; the correct symbol here is $=$.

In Example 3.7 we solved the equation $x(x-2) = 3$; we showed that its solution set is $\{-1, 3\}$. The forward ($\Rightarrow$) part of the proof shows that if x satisfies $x(x-2) = 3$, then $x = -1$ or $x = 3$; in other words, these are the only possible solutions of the equation. The backward ($\Leftarrow$) part shows that if $x = -1$ or $x = 3$ then x satisfies $x(x-2) = 3$; in other words, these two values actually are solutions of the equation. The symbol $\Leftrightarrow$ is the one to use when solving equations or inequalities, and you must be sure that its use is valid at each step; in other words, that both implications hold.

In this subsection we have discussed proof in the context of how to prove implications (and equivalences—but an equivalence is just two implications). However, what we have said extends to proofs of other types of statements. A statement Q that is not an implication can be proved by building up a sequence of statements leading to Q in the way that we have seen for an implication, except that there is no assumption P to be made at the start. Instead the first statement in the sequence must be one that we know to be true from our previous mathematical knowledge.

> If you wanted to prove only that $x = -1$ and $x = 3$ are solutions, and not that they are the only solutions, then although you could do so by giving the backward part of the above proof, it would be more natural to simply substitute each of these values in turn into the equation.

> For example, statement 4 on page 36 is not an implication (nor an equivalence).

3.4 Counter-examples

Proving that an implication is true can be difficult. However, you may suspect that an implication is false, and it can often (but not always!) be easier to deal with this situation. To prove that an implication $P \Rightarrow Q$ is false, you just have to give *one* example of a case where the statement P is true but the statement Q is false. Such an example is called a **counter-example** to the implication. Here are two examples.

Example 3.8   Show that each of the following implications about integers is false, by giving counter-examples.

(a) If n is prime, then $2^n - 1$ is prime.

(b) If the product mn is a multiple of 4 then both m and n are multiples of 2.

Solution

(a) The number 11 is a counter-example, because 11 is prime but $2^{11} - 1 = 2047$, which is not prime, since $2047 = 23 \times 89$. Hence the implication is false.

> See the text below for how you might find this counter-example.

(b) Taking $m = 4$ and $n = 1$ provides a counter-example, because then $mn = 4$, which is a multiple of 4, but n is not a multiple of 2. Hence the implication is false.   ∎

There is no general method for finding counter-examples. For some statements, such as the statement in part (b) of the above example, a little thought about the statement should suggest a suitable counter-example. For other statements, the quickest method may just be to try out different values for the variable (or variables) until you hit on a counter-example. For example, for the statement in part (a) of the above example, we can repeatedly choose a prime number n, calculate $2^n - 1$ and check whether it is prime.

> Remember that just *one* counter-example is sufficient. For example, you can show that the statement
> > if $x^2 > 4$ then $x > 2$
> is false by considering the value $x = -3$. There is no need to show that every number x less than -2 is a counter-example, even though this is true.

In order to carry out this procedure for Example 3.8(a), we need a method for checking whether a given number m is prime. We could simply check whether m is divisible by each of the integers between 2 and $m - 1$, inclusive, but this involves a large amount of calculation even for fairly small integers m.

We can significantly reduce the amount of calculation needed by using the following fact, which holds for any integer $m \geq 2$:

> If m is not divisible by any of the primes less than or equal to $\sqrt{m}$, then m is a prime number.

You will be asked to prove this statement later in this section. Here is an example of its use.

Example 3.9   Show that 127 is a prime number.

Solution $\sqrt{127} = 11.3$, to one decimal place, so the primes less than or equal to $\sqrt{127}$ are $2, 3, 5, 7$ and 11. Dividing 127 by each of these in turn gives a non-integer answer in each case, so 127 is prime.   ■

If this procedure is applied to a number that is not prime, then it will yield a prime factor.

> **Exercise 3.6**   Give a counter-example to disprove each of the following implications.
>
> (a) If $m + n$ is even, then both m and n are even.
>
> (b) If $x < 2$ then $(x^2 - 2)^2 < 4$.
>
> (c) If n is a positive integer, then $4^n + 1$ is prime.

As with implications, you may suspect that an equivalence is false. To prove that an equivalence $P \Leftrightarrow Q$ is false, you have to show that at least one of the implications $P \Rightarrow Q$ and $Q \Rightarrow P$ is false, which you can do by providing a counter-example.

3.5 Proof by induction

Mathematical induction is a method of proof that is useful for proving many statements involving integers. Consider, for example, the statement

$$1 + 3 + \cdots + (2n - 1) = n^2 \text{ for all positive integers } n.$$

Let us denote the statement

$$1 + 3 + \cdots + (2n - 1) = n^2$$

by $P(n)$. It is easy to check that $P(n)$ is true for small values of n; for example

$$1 = 1^2,$$
$$1 + 3 = 4 = 2^2,$$
$$1 + 3 + 5 = 9 = 3^2,$$

so certainly $P(1)$, $P(2)$ and $P(3)$ are all true. But how can we prove that $P(n)$ is true for all positive integers n?

This type of notation, in which a symbol denoting a statement is followed by a symbol denoting a variable, in brackets, is useful for a variable proposition (a statement that is true or false possibly depending on the value of a variable).

The method of induction works like this. Suppose that we wish to prove that a statement $P(n)$, such as the one above, is true for all positive integers n. Now suppose that we have proved that the following two statements are true.

1. $P(1)$
2. If $P(k)$ is true, then so is $P(k + 1)$, for $k = 1, 2, \ldots$.

Let us consider what we can deduce from this. Certainly $P(1)$ is true, because that is statement 1. Also $P(2)$ is true, because by statement 2, if $P(1)$ is true, then so is $P(2)$. Similarly, $P(3)$ is true, since $P(2)$ is. Since this process goes on for ever, we can deduce that $P(n)$ is true for all positive integers n. We thus have the following method.

> **Principle of Mathematical Induction**   To prove that a statement $P(n)$ is true for $n = 1, 2, \ldots$.
> 1. Show that $P(1)$ is true.
> 2. Show that the implication $P(k) \Rightarrow P(k+1)$ is true for $k = 1, 2, \ldots$.

Mathematical induction is often compared to pushing over a line of dominoes. Imagine a (possibly infinite!) line of dominoes set up in such a way that if any one domino falls then the next domino in line will fall too—this is analogous to step 2 above. Now imagine pushing over the first domino—this is analogous to step 1. The result is that *all* the dominoes fall!

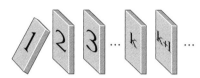

In the next example we apply mathematical induction to prove the statement mentioned at the beginning of this subsection.

This statement also appeared in the list of statements at the beginning of Subsection 3.1.

Example 3.10   Prove that $1 + 3 + \cdots + (2n - 1) = n^2$, for $n = 1, 2, \ldots$.

Solution   Let $P(n)$ be the statement $1 + 3 + \cdots + (2n - 1) = n^2$.

Then $P(1)$ is true, because $1 = 1^2$.

Now let $k \geq 1$, and assume that $P(k)$ is true; that is,

$$1 + 3 + \cdots + (2k - 1) = k^2.$$

We wish to deduce that $P(k + 1)$ is true; that is,

$$1 + 3 + \cdots + (2k + 1) = (k + 1)^2.$$

Now

The final term on the left-hand side here is
$2(k+1) - 1 = 2k + 1.$

$$
\begin{aligned}
1 + 3 + \cdots + (2k + 1) &= (1 + 3 + \cdots + (2k - 1)) + (2k + 1) \\
&= k^2 + (2k + 1) \quad \text{(by } P(k)) \\
&= (k + 1)^2.
\end{aligned}
$$

Hence

$$P(k) \Rightarrow P(k + 1), \text{ for } k = 1, 2, \ldots.$$

Hence, by mathematical induction, $P(n)$ is true, for $n = 1, 2, \ldots$.   ∎

Exercise 3.7   Prove each of the following statements by mathematical induction.
(a) $1 + 2 + \cdots + n = \frac{1}{2}n(n + 1)$, for $n = 1, 2, \ldots$.
(b) $1^3 + 2^3 + \cdots + n^3 = \frac{1}{4}n^2(n + 1)^2$, for $n = 1, 2, \ldots$.

In the next example, we need to be careful to carry out appropriate algebraic manipulation so that we can use $P(k)$ to prove $P(k + 1)$.

Example 3.11   Prove that $2^{3n+1} + 5$ is a multiple of 7, for $n = 1, 2, \ldots$.

Solution   Let $P(n)$ be the statement

$2^{3n+1} + 5$ is a multiple of 7.

Then $P(1)$ is true, because $2^{3 \times 1 + 1} + 5 = 2^4 + 5 = 21 = 3 \times 7$.

Now let $k \geq 1$, and assume that $P(k)$ is true; that is,

$2^{3k+1} + 5$ is a multiple of 7.

We wish to deduce that $P(k+1)$ is true; that is,

$2^{3(k+1)+1} + 5 = 2^{3k+4} + 5$ is a multiple of 7.

Now

$$2^{3k+4} + 5 = 2^3 2^{3k+1} + 5$$
$$= 8 \times 2^{3k+1} + 5$$
$$= 7 \times 2^{3k+1} + 2^{3k+1} + 5.$$

The first term here is a multiple of 7, and $2^{3k+1} + 5$ is a multiple of 7, by $P(k)$. Therefore $2^{3k+4} + 5$ is a multiple of 7. Hence

$P(k) \Rightarrow P(k+1)$, for $k = 1, 2, \ldots$.

Hence, by mathematical induction, $P(n)$ is true, for $n = 1, 2, \ldots$. ■

> The first manipulation is intended to create the sub-expression 2^{3k+1} in the expression, so we can use $P(k)$.

Mathematical induction can be adapted to deal with situations that differ a little from the standard one. For example, if a statement $P(n)$ is not true for $n = 1$ but we wish to prove that it is true for $n = 2, 3, \ldots$, then we can do this by following the usual method, except that in step 1 we prove that $P(2)$, rather than $P(1)$, is true. (Also, in step 2 we have to show that $P(k) \Rightarrow P(k+1)$ for $k = 2, 3 \ldots$, rather than for $k = 1, 2, \ldots$.) In the next example we prove that a statement is true for $n = 7, 8, \ldots$.

> This is analogous to pushing over the second domino in the line: the result is that all the dominoes except the first fall!

Example 3.12   Prove that $3^n < n!$ for all $n \geq 7$.

Solution   Let $P(n)$ be the statement $3^n < n!$.

Then $P(7)$ is true, because $3^7 = 2187 < 5040 = 7!$.

> $P(n)$ is false for $n = 1, 2, \ldots, 6$.

Now let $k \geq 7$, and assume that $P(k)$ is true; that is,

$3^k < k!$.

We wish to deduce that $P(k+1)$ is true; that is,

$3^{k+1} < (k+1)!$.

Now

$$3^{k+1} = 3 \times 3^k$$
$$< 3 \times k! \quad \text{(by } P(k))$$
$$< (k+1)k! \quad \text{(because } k \geq 7, \text{ and hence } k+1 \geq 8 > 3)$$
$$= (k+1)!.$$

Hence $P(k) \Rightarrow P(k+1)$, for $k = 7, 8, \ldots$.

Hence, by mathematical induction, $P(n)$ is true, for $n = 7, 8, \ldots$. ■

> **Exercise 3.8**   Prove each of the following statements by mathematical induction.
>
> (a) $4^{2n-3} + 1$ is a multiple of 5, for $n = 2, 3, \ldots$.
>
> (b) $5^n < n!$ for all $n \geq 12$.

3.6 Proof by contradiction

Sometimes a useful approach to proving a statement is to ask yourself, 'Well, what if the statement were false?'. Consider the following example.

Example 3.13   Prove that there is no positive real number a such that

$$a + \frac{1}{a} < 2.$$

Solution   Suppose that there *is* a positive real number a such that

$$a + \frac{1}{a} < 2.$$

Then, since a is positive, we have

$$a\left(a + \frac{1}{a}\right) < 2a,$$

which, on multiplying out and rearranging, gives

$$a^2 - 2a + 1 < 0; \quad \text{that is,} \quad (a-1)^2 < 0.$$

But this is impossible, since the square of every real number is greater than or equal to zero. Hence we can conclude that there is no such real number a. ■

The above proof is an example of **proof by contradiction**. The idea is that if we wish to prove that a statement Q is true, then we begin by *assuming* that Q is *false*. We then attempt to deduce, using the method of a sequence of statements that you saw in Subsection 3.3, a statement that is definitely false, which in this context is called a *contradiction*. If this can be achieved, then since everything about our argument is valid except possibly the assumption that Q is false, and yet we have deduced a contradiction, we can conclude that the assumption is in fact false – in other words, Q is true.

Here is a classic proof by contradiction, which was given by Euclid in about 300 BC.

This was a favourite proof of the Cambridge mathematician G. H. Hardy (1877–1947), who described proof by contradiction as 'one of a mathematician's finest weapons'.

Example 3.14   Prove that there are infinitely many prime numbers.

Solution   Suppose that there are only finitely many primes,

$$p_1, p_2, \ldots, p_n.$$

Consider the integer

$$N = p_1 p_2 p_3 \cdots p_n + 1.$$

This integer is greater than each of the primes $p_1, p_2, \ldots, p_n$, so it is not prime. Therefore it has a prime factor, p, say. Now p cannot be any of the primes $p_1, p_2, \ldots, p_n$, since dividing any one of these into N leaves the remainder 1. Thus, p is a prime other than $p_1, p_2, \ldots, p_n$. This is a contradiction, so our supposition must be false. It follows that there are infinitely many primes. ■

We are using the Fundamental Theorem of Arithmetic to deduce that N has a prime factor.

> **Exercise 3.9**   Use proof by contradiction to prove each of the following statements.
>
> (a) There are no real numbers a and b with $ab > \frac{1}{2}(a^2 + b^2)$.
>
> (b) There are no integers m and n with $5m + 15n = 357$.

To prove an implication $P \Rightarrow Q$ using proof by contradiction, you should begin by assuming that P is true in the usual way. Then you should assume, hoping for a contradiction, that Q is false. If under these assumptions you can deduce a contradiction, then you can conclude that if P is true, then Q must also be true, which is the required implication. Here is an example.

Example 3.15   Prove that if $n = a \times b$ where $n > 0$, then at least one of a and b is less than or equal to $\sqrt{n}$.

Solution   Suppose that $n = a \times b$ where $n > 0$. Suppose also that $a > \sqrt{n}$ and $b > \sqrt{n}$. Then

$$n = ab > (\sqrt{n})(\sqrt{n}) = n;$$

that is, $n > n$. This contradiction shows that the supposition that $a > \sqrt{n}$ and $b > \sqrt{n}$ must be false; that is, at least one of a and b is less than or equal to $\sqrt{n}$. ∎

Exercise 3.10   Use proof by contradiction to prove that if $n = a + 2b$, where a and b are positive real numbers, then $a \geq \frac{1}{2}n$ or $b \geq \frac{1}{4}n$.

3.7 Proof by contraposition

Given any implication, we can form another implication, called its **contrapositive**, which is equivalent to the original implication. The contrapositive of the implication 'if P, then Q' is 'if not Q, then not P', where 'not P' and 'not Q' denote the negations of the statements P and Q, respectively. For example, the contrapositive of the implication

   if x is an integer, then x^2 is an integer

is the implication

   if x^2 is not an integer, then x is not an integer.

You can think of an implication and its contrapositive as asserting the same thing, but in different ways. You should take a few moments to convince yourself of this in the case of the implication and its contrapositive given above. Try this also with the non-mathematical example in the margin!

Since an implication and its contrapositive are equivalent, if you have proved one, then you have proved the other. Sometimes the easiest way to prove an implication is to prove its contrapositive instead. This is called *proof by contraposition*. Here is an example. The proof makes use of the fact that

$$x^n - 1 = (x - 1)(x^{n-1} + x^{n-2} + \cdots + x + 1), \tag{3.1}$$

for any real number x and any positive integer n. This can be verified by multiplying out the right-hand side. (Try it!)

Example 3.16   Prove the following implication about positive integers n:

   if $2^n - 1$ is prime, then n is prime.

Solution   We shall prove the contrapositive of the implication, which is

   if n is not prime, then $2^n - 1$ is not prime.

Suppose that n is a positive integer that is not prime. If $n = 1$, then $2^n - 1 = 2 - 1 = 1$, which is not prime. Otherwise $n = ab$, where $1 < a, b < n$. Hence

$$2^n - 1 = 2^{ab} - 1$$
$$= (2^a)^b - 1$$
$$= (2^a - 1)((2^a)^{b-1} + \cdots + 2^a + 1),$$

Here is another example: the contrapositive of the implication
   if Rosie is a sheep, then Rosie is less than two metres tall
is
   if Rosie is not less than two metres tall, then Rosie is not a sheep
or, more simply,
   if Rosie's height is two metres or more, then Rosie is not a sheep.

In this proof we consider two cases separately: the cases $n = 1$ and $n > 1$. Splitting into cases is sometimes an effective way to proceed in a proof.

where the last line follows from equation (3.1). Now $2^a - 1 > 1$, since $a > 1$, and similarly $(2^a)^{b-1} + \cdots + 2^a + 1 > 1$, since both a and b are greater than 1. Hence $2^n - 1$ is not prime. We have thus proved the required contrapositive implication in both the cases $n = 1$ and $n > 1$. Hence the original implication is also true.   ■

We put $x = 2^a$ and $n = b$ in equation (3.1).

Exercise 3.11   Use proof by contraposition to prove each of the following statements about integers m and n.

(a) If n^3 is even, then n is even.

(b) If mn is odd, then both m and n are odd.

(c) If an integer $n > 1$ is not divisible by any of the primes less than or equal to $\sqrt{n}$, then n is a prime number.

We used this result in Subsection 3.4.

  Hint: Use the result of Example 3.15, on page 48.

3.8 Universal and existential statements

Many mathematical statements include the phrase 'for all', or another form of words with the same meaning. Here are a few examples.

  $x^2 \geq 0$ *for all* real numbers x.

  Every multiple of 6 is divisible by 3.

  $1 + 3 + 5 + \cdots + (2n - 1) = n^2$ *for each* positive integer n.

  Any rational number is a real number.

Statements of this type are known as *universal* statements, and the phrase 'for all', and its equivalents, are referred to as the *universal quantifier*.

Statements that begin with a phrase like 'There are no . . . ' or 'There does not exist . . .' are universal statements, because they can be rephrased in terms of 'For all'. For example, the statement

  there is no integer n such that $n^2 = 3$

can be rephrased as

  for all integers n, $n^2 \neq 3$.

The universal quantifier is sometimes denoted by the symbol $\forall$; for example, the first universal statement above might be abbreviated as

  $\forall x \in \mathbb{R},\ x^2 \geq 0,$

which is read as 'for all x in $\mathbb{R}$, x squared is greater than or equal to zero'.

Other mathematical statements may include the phrase 'there exists', or another form of words with the same meaning. Here are a few examples.

  There exists a real number that is not a rational number.

  There is a real number x such that $\cos x = x$.

  Some multiples of 3 are not divisible by 6.

  The equation $x^3 + x^2 + 5 = 0$ has *at least one* real solution.

In mathematics, the word *some* is used to mean 'at least one', rather than 'several'.

Statements of this type are known as *existential* statements, and the phrase 'there exists' and its equivalents are referred to as the *existential quantifier*.

In natural language, the word 'any' may mean either 'every' or 'at least one', as in 'any fool could do that' and 'did you prove any theorems?'. In mathematics, the meaning depends on the context in a similar way. We try to avoid using 'any' where it might cause confusion.

The existential quantifier is sometimes denoted by the symbol $\exists$; for example, the second existential statement above might be abbreviated as

  $\exists x \in \mathbb{R}$ such that $\cos x = x,$

which is read as 'there exists x in $\mathbb{R}$ such that $\cos x$ equals x'.

We saw earlier in this section that it is often necessary to negate statements, for example when we wish to use proof by contradiction or proof by contraposition.

The negation of universal and existential statements needs to be treated with particular care. The negation of a universal statement is an existential statement, and vice versa. This is illustrated by the examples in the table below. You saw further examples in Example 3.1(a), and Exercises 3.1(c) and (d).

Statement	Negation
Every integer is a real number.	There exists an integer that is not a real number.
There is an even prime number.	Every prime number is odd.
The equation $x^2 + 4 = 0$ has a real solution.	The equation $x^2 + 4 = 0$ has no real solutions.

You may have found some of the ideas in this section difficult to get used to—this is to be expected, since reading and understanding mathematics, and writing mathematics clearly and accurately, can both be difficult at first. Your skills will improve as you gain experience. To accelerate this improvement, you should, when reading mathematics, try to make sure that you gain a clear understanding of exactly what each statement asserts. When writing mathematics, you should try to be as clear and accurate as you can. Include enough detail to make the argument clear, but omit any statements that are not necessary to reach the required conclusion. A good check is to read over your work and ask yourself whether you would be able to follow what you have written in six months' time, when you have forgotten the thoughts and rough work that led to it. Use the solutions to the examples and exercises in the course as models for good mathematical writing.

You may find it helpful to re-visit parts of Section 3 later in your study of the course.

Further exercises

Exercise 3.12   Which of the following statements have the same meaning?

(a) If n is even, then n^2 is a multiple of 4.

(b) n is even only if n^2 is a multiple of 4.

(c) n^2 is a multiple of 4 whenever n is even.

(d) $x > 0 \Rightarrow x^2 + 4x > 0$.

(e) $x > 0$ is necessary for $x^2 + 4x > 0$.

(f) $x > 0$ is sufficient for $x^2 + 4x > 0$.

Exercise 3.13   Determine whether the numbers 221 and 223 are prime.

Exercise 3.14   Prove, or give a counter-example to disprove, each of the following statements.

(a) If n is a positive integer, then $n^3 - n$ is even.

(b) If $m + n$ is a multiple of k, then m and n are multiples of k.

(c) If θ is a real number, then $\sin 2\theta = 2 \sin \theta$.

(d) The following function is one-one:

$$f : \mathbb{R} \longrightarrow \mathbb{R}$$
$$x \longmapsto 3x^2 - 6x + 1.$$

(e) The function g is the inverse of the function f, where f and g are given by

$$f : \mathbb{R} - \{1\} \longrightarrow \mathbb{R} - \{0\} \qquad g : \mathbb{R} - \{0\} \longrightarrow \mathbb{R} - \{1\}$$
$$x \longmapsto \frac{1}{x - 1} \quad \text{and} \quad x \longmapsto 1 + \frac{1}{x}.$$

Exercise 3.15

(a) Write down the converse of the following statement.

  If m and n are both even integers, then $m - n$ is an even integer.

(b) Determine whether the original statement and the converse are true, and give a proof or counter-example, as appropriate.

Exercise 3.16   Prove each of the following statements by mathematical induction.

(a) $\dfrac{1}{1 \times 2} + \dfrac{1}{2 \times 3} + \cdots + \dfrac{1}{(n - 1)n} = \dfrac{n - 1}{n}$ for $n = 2, 3, \ldots$.

(b) The integer $3^{2n} - 1$ is divisible by 8 for $n = 1, 2, \ldots$.

Exercise 3.17   Prove by contradiction that $(a + b)^2 \geq 4ab$ for all real numbers a and b.

Exercise 3.18

(a) Write down the contrapositive of the following statement, for positive integers n.

  If n^2 is divisible by 3, then n is divisible by 3.

(b) Prove that the contrapositive is true, and hence that the original statement is true.

Exercise 3.19   Determine which of the following statements are true, and give a proof or counter-example as appropriate.

(a) For all $x, y \in \mathbb{R}$, $x < y \Rightarrow x^2 < y^2$.

(b) For all $x \in \mathbb{R}$, $x^2 - x = 2$.

(c) There exists $x \in \mathbb{R}$ such that $x^2 - x = 2$.

(d) There exists $x \in \mathbb{R}$ such that $x^2 - x = -1$.

(e) There are no real numbers x, y for which x/y and y/x are both integers.

(f) For all positive integers n,

$$1^2 + 2^2 + 3^2 + \cdots + n^2 = \tfrac{1}{6}n(n + 1)(2n + 1).$$

(g) For all positive integers $n \geq 2$,

$$\left(1 - \frac{1}{2}\right)\left(1 - \frac{1}{3}\right) \cdots \left(1 - \frac{1}{n}\right) = \frac{1}{2n}.$$

4 Two identities

After working through this section, you should be able to:

(a) understand and use the Binomial Theorem;

(b) understand and use the Geometric Series Identity;

(c) understand and use the Polynomial Factorisation Theorem.

An **identity** is an equation involving variables which is true for all possible values of the variables. You will already be familiar with many basic identities, such as

$$(a + b)^2 = a^2 + 2ab + b^2 \quad \text{and} \quad a^2 - b^2 = (a - b)(a + b).$$

These identities are particular cases of more general identities that we shall use extensively later in the course. In this section we state and prove these key identities, using some of the techniques described earlier in the unit.

Some texts use the symbol $\equiv$ to denote an identity, but we shall not do so.

4.1 The Binomial Theorem

A striking mathematical pattern appears when we expand expressions of the form $(a + b)^n$ for $n = 1, 2, \ldots$:

$(a + b)^1 = a^1 + b^1,$

$(a + b)^2 = a^2 + 2ab + b^2,$

$(a + b)^3 = (a + b)(a^2 + 2ab + b^2) = a^3 + 3a^2b + 3ab^2 + b^3,$

$(a + b)^4 = (a + b)(a^3 + 3a^2b + 3ab^2 + b^3) = a^4 + 4a^3b + 6a^2b^2 + 4ab^3 + b^4,$

and so on. The coefficients that appear in these expansions can be arranged as a triangular table, in which 1s appear on the left and right edges, and the remaining entries can be generated by using the rule that each inner entry is the sum of the two nearest entries in the row above.

For example, $10 = 4 + 6$.

$(a + b)^0$					1					
$(a + b)^1$				1		1				
$(a + b)^2$			1		2		1			
$(a + b)^3$		1		3		3		1		
$(a + b)^4$	1		4		6		4		1	
$(a + b)^5$	1	5		10		10		5		1

The 1 at the top corresponds to $n = 0$:

$$(a + b)^0 = 1.$$

This table is known as *Pascal's triangle*, after the French mathematician, physicist and theologian Blaise Pascal (1623–1662), although it appeared several hundred years earlier in a book by the Chinese mathematician Chu Shih-Chieh.

We can calculate any coefficient in Pascal's triangle directly, instead of from two coefficients in the row above, because the coefficients in the row corresponding to $(a + b)^n$ are given by

$$\binom{n}{0}, \binom{n}{1}, \ldots, \binom{n}{n}, \quad \text{where} \quad \binom{n}{k} = \frac{n!}{k!\,(n - k)!}.$$

The expression $\binom{n}{k}$ was introduced in Subsection 1.5, where we saw that it gives the number of different k-element subsets of an n-element set.

For example, the fourth coefficient in the row corresponding to $(a + b)^5$ is given by

$$\binom{5}{3} = \frac{5!}{3!\,2!} = 10.$$

Example 1.5 shows why the numbers $\binom{n}{k}$ satisfy the rule described above for generating Pascal's triangle.

Here is the general formula for the expansion of $(a + b)^n$. It is our first key identity.

Theorem 4.1 Binomial Theorem

Let $a, b \in \mathbb{R}$ and let n be a positive integer. Then

$$(a+b)^n = \binom{n}{0} a^n + \binom{n}{1} a^{n-1}b + \cdots + \binom{n}{k} a^{n-k}b^k + \cdots + \binom{n}{n} b^n.$$

Note that

$$\binom{n}{0} = \binom{n}{n} = 1,$$

since $0! = 1$.

Proof   The shortest way of proving this result is to note that $(a + b)^n$ is the product of n brackets:

$$(a + b)^n = (a + b) \times (a + b) \times \cdots \times (a + b).$$

When this product is multiplied out, we find that each term of the form $a^{n-k}b^k$ arises by choosing the variable a from $n - k$ of the brackets and the variable b from the remaining k brackets. Thus the coefficient of $a^{n-k}b^k$ is equal to the number of ways of choosing a subset of $n - k$ brackets (or, equivalently, a subset of k brackets) from the set of n brackets, and this is precisely $\binom{n}{k}$, as required.   ∎

Note the following important special case of Theorem 4.1, obtained by taking $a = 1$ and $b = x$:

$$(1 + x)^n = \binom{n}{0} + \binom{n}{1} x + \cdots + \binom{n}{k} x^k + \cdots + \binom{n}{n} x^n$$

$$= 1 + nx + \frac{n(n-1)}{2!} x^2 + \cdots + x^n.$$

Example 4.1   Expand $(2 + 3x)^5$.

Solution   Using the Binomial Theorem with $n = 5$, $a = 2$ and $b = 3x$, we obtain

$$(2 + 3x)^5 = \binom{5}{0} 2^5 + \binom{5}{1} 2^4(3x) + \binom{5}{2} 2^3(3x)^2$$

$$+ \binom{5}{3} 2^2(3x)^3 + \binom{5}{4} 2(3x)^4 + \binom{5}{5} (3x)^5$$

$$= 2^5 + 5 \times 2^4(3x) + 10 \times 2^3(3x)^2$$

$$+ 10 \times 2^2(3x)^3 + 5 \times 2(3x)^4 + (3x)^5$$

$$= 32 + 240x + 720x^2 + 1080x^3 + 810x^4 + 243x^5.   ∎$$

Exercise 4.1   Find the coefficient of:

(a) $a^5 b^4$ in the expansion of $(a + b)^9$;

(b) x^4 in the expansion of $(1 + 2x)^5$.

Many identities can be obtained as special cases of the Binomial Theorem by choosing particular values for the variables a and b.

Example 4.2   Deduce from the Binomial Theorem that

$$2^n = \binom{n}{0} + \binom{n}{1} + \cdots + \binom{n}{k} + \cdots + \binom{n}{n}, \quad \text{for } n \geq 1.$$

Solution   Taking $a = 1$ and $b = 1$ in the statement of the Binomial Theorem, we obtain $(1 + 1)^n = 2^n$ on the left-hand side, whereas all the powers of a and b on the right-hand side are equal to 1. This gives the required identity.   ∎

In Subsection 1.5 we proved that a set with n elements has 2^n subsets. The identity in Example 4.2 provides an alternative proof of this fact. Since $\binom{n}{k}$ gives the number of k-element subsets of a set with n elements, the sum

$$\binom{n}{0} + \binom{n}{1} + \cdots + \binom{n}{k} + \cdots + \binom{n}{n}$$

gives the total number of subsets (of *all* sizes) of a set with n elements. By the identity in Example 4.2, this sum is equal to 2^n.

Exercise 4.2

(a) Use the Binomial Theorem to obtain an expansion for $(a - b)^n$.

(b) Write down the identity you obtain by taking $a = 1$ and $b = 1$ in part (a), and check that this identity is true for $n = 4$.

It is a remarkable fact that there is a version of the Binomial Theorem which holds when n is a real number, rather than just a positive integer. This general version, which involves an infinite series, was used by Isaac Newton, but a correct proof was not given until the early 19th century by the Norwegian mathematician Niels Abel.

A proof of this infinite version is given later in the course.

4.2 The Geometric Series Identity

Expressions of the form $a^n - b^n$ occur often in mathematics, and we can factorise them in the following simple manner:

$$a^2 - b^2 = (a - b)(a + b),$$
$$a^3 - b^3 = (a - b)(a^2 + ab + b^2),$$
$$a^4 - b^4 = (a - b)(a^3 + a^2b + ab^2 + b^3),$$

and so on. The following general result can be proved by multiplying out the expression on the right-hand side.

Theorem 4.2 Geometric Series Identity

Let $a, b \in \mathbb{R}$ and let n be a positive integer. Then

$$a^n - b^n = (a - b)(a^{n-1} + a^{n-2}b + \cdots + ab^{n-2} + b^{n-1}).$$

Exercise 4.3

(a) Write down the Geometric Series Identity in full for the case $n = 5$.

(b) Use the Geometric Series Identity to show that

$$a^n + b^n = (a + b)(a^{n-1} - a^{n-2}b + \cdots - ab^{n-2} + b^{n-1}),$$

where $a, b \in \mathbb{R}$ and n is an *odd* positive integer. Write down this identity in full for the case $n = 5$.

Theorem 4.2 has some useful consequences. In particular, it includes as a special case the following formula for the sum of a finite geometric series with initial term a, common ratio r, and n terms.

This explains the name of Theorem 4.2.

Corollary   Sum of a finite geometric series

Let $a, r \in \mathbb{R}$ and let n be a positive integer. Then

$$a + ar + ar^2 + \cdots + ar^{n-1} = \begin{cases} a\left(\dfrac{1 - r^n}{1 - r}\right), & \text{if } r \neq 1, \\ na, & \text{if } r = 1. \end{cases}$$

Recall that a *corollary* is a consequence of a theorem, proved by a short additional argument.

Proof   For the case $r \neq 1$, we need to show that

$$1 + r + r^2 + \cdots + r^{n-1} = \frac{1 - r^n}{1 - r};$$

that is,

$$1 - r^n = (1 - r)(1 + r + r^2 + \cdots + r^{n-1}).$$

But this follows from the statement of Theorem 4.2 with $a = 1$ and $b = r$.

When $r = 1$, the required identity is evident, since the left-hand side then consists of n terms all equal to a. ∎

Exercise 4.4   Find the sum of the following finite geometric series:

$$1 + 1/2 + 1/4 + \cdots + 1/2^{n-1}.$$

Theorem 4.2 can also be used to give a short proof of a useful result which helps us to factorise polynomials.

A polynomial in x of degree n is an expression of the form
$$a_n x^n + a_{n-1} x^{n-1} + \cdots$$
$$+ a_1 x + a_0,$$
where $a_n \neq 0$.

Theorem 4.3 Polynomial Factorisation Theorem

Let $p(x)$ be a polynomial of degree n, and let $\alpha \in \mathbb{R}$. Then $p(\alpha) = 0$ if and only if

$$p(x) = (x - \alpha)q(x), \tag{4.1}$$

where q is a polynomial of degree $n - 1$.

Proof   First, we prove the 'if' part.

If equation (4.1) holds, then $p(\alpha) = (\alpha - \alpha)q(\alpha) = 0$.

Here we prove an equivalence by proving separately the two implications that it comprises.

Next, we prove the 'only if' part.

Suppose that $p(\alpha) = 0$. Let $p(x) = a_n x^n + a_{n-1} x^{n-1} + \cdots + a_1 x + a_0$, where $a_n \neq 0$. Since $p(\alpha) = 0$,

$$
\begin{aligned}
p(x) &= p(x) - p(\alpha) \\
&= (a_n x^n + a_{n-1} x^{n-1} + \cdots + a_1 x + a_0) \\
&\quad - (a_n \alpha^n + a_{n-1} \alpha^{n-1} + \cdots + a_1 \alpha + a_0) \\
&= a_n(x^n - \alpha^n) + a_{n-1}(x^{n-1} - \alpha^{n-1}) + \cdots + a_1(x - \alpha),
\end{aligned}
$$

since the constant terms a_0 cancel. Now, by Theorem 4.2, each of the bracketed expressions in this last expression has factor $x - \alpha$, so $p(x)$ is the product of $x - \alpha$ and a polynomial of the form

$$
q(x) = a_n x^{n-1} + \cdots,
$$

which has degree $n - 1$.   ∎

Although the proof of Theorem 4.3 could be used to find the polynomial $q(x)$, it is usually easier to find this polynomial by comparing coefficients, once we know that $x - \alpha$ is a factor.

Example 4.3   Show that $x - 2$ is a factor of the cubic polynomial

$$
p(x) = x^3 + x^2 - x - 10,
$$

and find the corresponding factorisation of $p(x)$.

Solution   First, we evaluate $p(2)$:

$$
p(2) = 2^3 + 2^2 - 2 - 10 = 8 + 4 - 2 - 10 = 0.
$$

Therefore, by the Polynomial Factorisation Theorem, $p(x)$ has the factor $x - 2$. By comparing the coefficients of x^3, and by comparing the constant terms, we obtain

$$
x^3 + x^2 - x - 10 = (x - 2)(x^2 + cx + 5), \quad \text{for some number } c.
$$

The coefficient of x^2 is 1 on the left-hand side, and $-2 + c$ on the right-hand side, so $c = 3$, which gives

$$
x^3 + x^2 - x - 10 = (x - 2)(x^2 + 3x + 5). \quad ∎
$$

We obtain this by noting that the coefficient of x^2 in the quadratic expression on the right-hand side must be 1 in order to give 1 as the coefficient of x^3 on the left-hand side. Similarly, the constant term in the quadratic expression must be 5 to give the constant term -10 on the left-hand side.

Exercise 4.5   For what value of c is $x + 3$ a factor of

$$
p(x) = x^3 + cx^2 + 6x + 36 \, ?
$$

The following result about polynomial factorisation can be proved by applying the Polynomial Factorisation Theorem repeatedly, although we omit the details here. We have taken the coefficient of the highest power of x to be 1, for simplicity. The **roots** of a polynomial $p(x)$ are the solutions of the equation $p(x) = 0$.

The roots of a polynomial are also known as its *zeros*.

Corollary   Let $p(x) = x^n + a_{n-1} x^{n-1} + \cdots + a_1 x + a_0$, and suppose that $p(x)$ has n distinct real roots, $\alpha_1, \alpha_2, \ldots, \alpha_n$. Then

$$
p(x) = (x - \alpha_1)(x - \alpha_2) \cdots (x - \alpha_n). \tag{4.2}
$$

In fact, as you will see in Unit I3, *every* polynomial of the form

$$p(x) = x^n + a_{n-1}x^{n-1} + \cdots + a_1x + a_0$$

has a factorisation of the form (4.2), although the roots $\alpha_1, \alpha_2, \ldots, \alpha_n$ need not be distinct and may include non-real *complex numbers*. (Complex numbers are introduced in Unit I3.) It follows that a polynomial of degree n has at most n distinct roots.

Two useful consequences of this factorisation of $p(x)$ are

$$a_{n-1} = -(\alpha_1 + \alpha_2 + \cdots + \alpha_n) \tag{4.3}$$

and

$$a_0 = (-1)^n \alpha_1 \alpha_2 \cdots \alpha_n. \tag{4.4}$$

We obtain the first of these equations by comparing the coefficients of x^{n-1} on the two sides of the equation

$$x^n + a_{n-1}x^{n-1} + \cdots + a_1x + a_0 = (x - \alpha_1)(x - \alpha_2) \cdots (x - \alpha_n). \tag{4.5}$$

When the expression on the right-hand side of equation (4.5) is multiplied out, each term in x^{n-1} arises by choosing the variable x from $n-1$ of the brackets, and the constant term from the remaining bracket. Choosing the constant term from the first bracket gives $-\alpha_1 x^{n-1}$, choosing the constant term from the second bracket gives $-\alpha_2 x^{n-1}$, and so on. Adding all these terms and comparing the resulting total coefficient with the coefficient of x^{n-1} on the left-hand side of equation (4.5) gives equation (4.3). Equation (4.4) is obtained by comparing the constant terms on each side of equation (4.5).

Equations (4.3) and (4.4) relate the sum and product of the roots of the polynomial $p(x)$ to two of its coefficients, and they provide a useful check on the values of the roots found. Equation (4.4) is useful if you suspect that a polynomial of the form $p(x) = x^n + a_{n-1}x^{n-1} + \cdots + a_1x + a_0$ has n roots all of which are are integers; if they are, then each of the roots must be a factor of the constant coefficient a_0.

For example,
$$x^4 - 6x^3 + 9x^2 + 4x - 12$$
$$= (x - 2)(x - 2)(x - 3)(x + 1).$$

In the above polynomial, the coefficient of x^3 is
$$-6 = -(2 + 2 + 3 - 1),$$
and the constant term is
$$-12 = (-1)^4 \times 2 \times 2 \times 3 \times (-1).$$

Example 4.4   Solve the following equation, given that all the solutions are integers.

$$p(x) = x^3 - 6x^2 - 9x + 14 = 0.$$

Solution   Since all the roots of $p(x)$ are integers, the only possible roots are the factors of 14, that is, $\pm 1, \pm 2, \pm 7, \pm 14$. Considering these in turn, we obtain the following table.

x	1	-1	2	-2	7	-7	14	-14
$p(x)$	0	16	-20	0	0	-560	1456	-3780

The only solutions are $x = 1$, $x = -2$ and $x = 7$. So,

$$x^3 - 6x^2 - 9x + 14 = (x - 1)(x + 2)(x - 7). \quad \blacksquare$$

For a cubic equation, once we have found three roots, we do not need to complete the rest of the table, so we could have omitted the last three columns here.

Exercise 4.6

(a) Solve each of the following equations, given that all their solutions are integers.

(i) $p(x) = x^3 - 3x^2 + 4 = 0$
(ii) $p(x) = x^3 - 9x^2 + 23x - 15 = 0$

(b) Determine a polynomial equation whose solutions are $1, 2, 3, -3$.

Further exercises

Exercise 4.7   Determine the expansions of the following expressions.

(a) $(a + 3b)^4$

(b) $(1 - t)^7$

Exercise 4.8   Find the coefficients of the following.

(a) $a^3 b^7$ in the expansion of $(a + b)^{10}$

(b) x^{13} in the expansion of $(2 + x)^{15}$

Exercise 4.9   Find the sum of each of the following finite geometric series.

(a) $3 - 1 + \dfrac{1}{3} - \dfrac{1}{9} + \cdots - \dfrac{1}{3^{10}}$

(b) $1 + \dfrac{a}{b} + \dfrac{a^2}{b^2} + \cdots + \dfrac{a^n}{b^n}$, where $a, b \in \mathbb{R}$, $a \neq b$ and $b \neq 0$

Exercise 4.10

(a) Show that $2x^3 + x^2 - 13x + 6$ has a factor $x - 2$, and hence factorise this polynomial.

(b) Solve the equation $x^3 + 6x^2 + 3x - 10 = 0$.

(c) Find the solutions for x in terms of y of the equation

$$x^2 + x = y^2 + y.$$

Exercise 4.11

(a) Find a cubic polynomial for which the sum of the roots is 0, the product of the roots is -30, and one root is 3.

(b) Find the other two roots of the polynomial found in part (a).

Solutions to the exercises

1.1 (a) True: -2 is an integer.

(b) False: 5 is a natural number.

(c) False: 1.3 is the rational number $\frac{13}{10}$.

(d) False: $\frac{1}{2}$ is not a natural number.

(e) True: $-\pi$ is a real number.

(f) True: 2 is a rational number $\left(\frac{2}{1}\right)$.

1.2 (a) True: 1 is a member of the set given.

(b) True: the set $\{-9\}$ is a member of the set given.

(c) False: the number 9 belongs to the set given, but the set $\{9\}$ does not.

(d) False: $(0,1)$ is not a member of the set given.

(e) True: the set $\{0,1\}$ is a member of the set given.

1.3 (a) $\{k \in \mathbb{Z} : -2 < k < 1000\}$

(b) $\{x \in \mathbb{R} : 2 \le x \le 7\}$

(c) $\{x \in \mathbb{Q} : x > 0 \text{ and } x^2 > 2\}$

(d) $\{2n : n \in \mathbb{N}\}$

(e) $\{2^k : k \in \mathbb{Z}\}$

1.4 (a) $l = \{(x,y) \in \mathbb{R}^2 : y = 2x + 5\}$

(b)

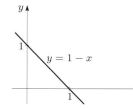

1.5 (a) $C = \{(x,y) \in \mathbb{R}^2 : (x-1)^2 + (y+4)^2 = 9\}$

(b)

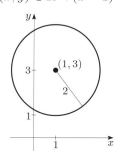

1.6 (a)

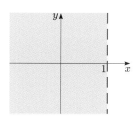

(b)

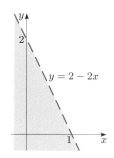

(c)

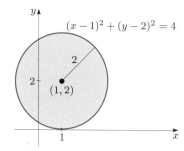

(d)

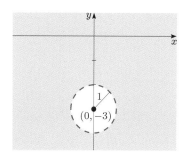

1.7 (a) $\{(x,y) \in \mathbb{R}^2 : 0 \le x \le 2, \ 1 \le y \le 3\}$

(b) $\{(x,y) \in \mathbb{R}^2 : x \ge 0, \ y = 2x^2 + 1\}$

1.8 (a) The set B consists of the solutions of the equation

$$x^2 + x - 6 = 0,$$

which we can write as

$$(x-2)(x+3) = 0.$$

So $B = \{2, -3\} = A$.

(b) $A = \{k \in \mathbb{Z} : k \text{ is odd and } 2 < k < 10\}$
$\quad\ = \{3,5,7,9\},$

$B = \{n \in \mathbb{N} : n \text{ is a prime number and } n < 10\}$
$\quad\ = \{2,3,5,7\}.$

Hence $A \ne B$, either because $2 \in B$ but $2 \notin A$, or because $9 \in A$ but $9 \notin B$.

1.9 (a) We calculate $x - 4y$ using the coordinates of each point of A:

$$5 - 4 \times 2 = -3,$$
$$1 - 4 \times 1 = -3,$$
$$-3 - 4 \times 0 = -3.$$

This shows that each element of A is an element of B, so $A \subseteq B$.

(b) The set A is the interior of the unit circle, and B is the half-plane consisting of all points with negative y-coordinate. So $A \not\subseteq B$, because, for example, the point $(\frac{1}{2}, \frac{1}{2})$ belongs to A but not to B.

1.10 We showed that $A \subseteq B$ in the solution to Exercise 1.9(a). Also, for example, the point $(9, 3)$ lies in B, since

$$9 - 4 \times 3 = -3,$$

but does not lie in A. Therefore A is a proper subset of B.

1.11 First we show that $A \subseteq B$.

Let $(x, y) \in A$; then $x = t^2$ and $y = 2t$, for some $t \in \mathbb{R}$. Hence $y^2 = 4t^2 = 4x$. So $(x, y) \in B$, and so $A \subseteq B$.

Next we show that $B \subseteq A$.

Let $(x, y) \in B$. We must show that $(x, y) \in A$. Let $t = \frac{1}{2}y$; then $x = \frac{1}{4}y^2 = \left(\frac{1}{2}y\right)^2 = t^2$, and $y = 2t$. So $(x, y) = (t^2, 2t) \in A$, and so $B \subseteq A$.

Since $A \subseteq B$ and $B \subseteq A$, it follows that $A = B$.

1.12

k	Subsets of $\{1, 2, 3, 4\}$ of size k
0	$\varnothing$
1	$\{1\}, \{2\}, \{3\}, \{4\}$
2	$\{1, 2\}, \{1, 3\}, \{1, 4\}, \{2, 3\}, \{2, 4\}, \{3, 4\}$
3	$\{1, 2, 3\}, \{1, 2, 4\}, \{1, 3, 4\}, \{2, 3, 4\}$
4	$\{1, 2, 3, 4\}$

The table shows that the set $\{1, 2, 3, 4\}$ has $1 + 4 + 6 + 4 + 1 = 16$ subsets in all.

1.13 $\binom{10}{2} = \dfrac{10!}{2!\, 8!} = \dfrac{10 \times 9}{2} = 5 \times 9 = 45,$

$\binom{10}{3} = \dfrac{10!}{3!\, 7!} = \dfrac{10 \times 9 \times 8}{3 \times 2} = 10 \times 3 \times 4 = 120,$

$\binom{11}{3} = \dfrac{11!}{3!\, 8!} = \dfrac{11 \times 10 \times 9}{3 \times 2} = 11 \times 5 \times 3 = 165.$

Hence $\binom{10}{2} + \binom{10}{3} = \binom{11}{3}.$

1.14 (a) $\binom{n}{n-k} = \dfrac{n!}{(n-k)!\, k!}$ and

$\binom{n}{k} = \dfrac{n!}{k!\, (n-k)!},$ so $\binom{n}{n-k} = \binom{n}{k}.$

(b) We can interpret the identity as follows.

$\binom{n}{k}$ is the number of ways of *choosing* k elements from n, which is the same as $\binom{n}{n-k}$, the number of ways of *excluding* k elements from n.

1.15 (a) $(1, 7) \cup [4, 11] = (1, 11].$

(b) The domain of f is the set

$$\{x \in \mathbb{R} : x^2 - 9 > 0\} = \{x \in \mathbb{R} : x < -3 \text{ or } x > 3\},$$

that is,

$$(-\infty, -3) \cup (3, \infty).$$

(c)

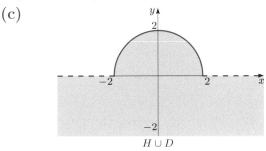

$H \cup D$

1.16 (a) $(1, 7) \cap [4, 11] = [4, 7).$

(b)

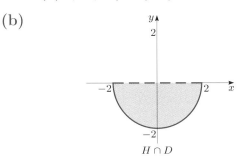

$H \cap D$

1.17 (a) $(1, 7) - [4, 11] = (1, 4)$ and $[4, 11] - (1, 7) = [7, 11].$

(b)

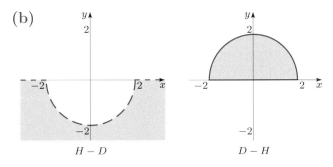

$H - D$ $\qquad$ $D - H$

1.18 (a) False: 0 is not a natural number.

(b) True: 0 is a rational number.

(c) False: -0.6 is a real number.

(d) True: 37 is an integer.

(e) False: 20 is not a member of the set given.

(f) True: the set $\{1, 2\}$ is the same as the set $\{2, 1\}$.

(g) False: $\varnothing$ does not contain any elements.

1.19 (a) The elements are $3, 4, 5, 6$. Note that 2 and 7 are not included.

(b) The elements are $-1, -4$. These are the solutions of the equation.

(c) The only element is 5. The equation has two solutions, -5 and 5, but only $5 \in \mathbb{N}$.

1.20 In each case, you may have found a different expression for the same set.

(a) $\{k \in \mathbb{Z} : -20 < k < -3\}$

(b) $\{3k : k \in \mathbb{Z}, \ k \neq 0\}$

(c) $\{x \in \mathbb{R} : x > 15\}$

1.21 (a)

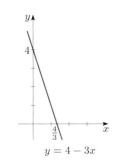

$y = 4 - 3x$

(b)

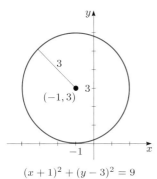

$(x + 1)^2 + (y - 3)^2 = 9$

(c)

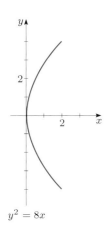

$y^2 = 8x$

1.22 (a)

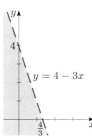

$y = 4 - 3x$

The line is not part of the set.

(b)

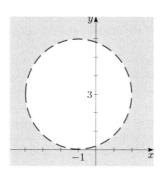

The circle is not part of the set.

(c)

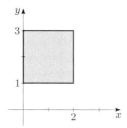

The edges of the square belong to the set.

1.23 (a) $(0, 0)$, $(0, 6)$ and $(-4, 6)$ all satisfy the equation $(x + 2)^2 + (y - 3)^2 = 13$, so $A \subseteq B$.

(b) The point $(1, 0)$ belongs to A but not to B, so A is not a subset of B.

(c) If $x = 2\cos t$ and $y = 3\sin t$, then $\dfrac{x^2}{4} + \dfrac{y^2}{9} = 1$, so $A \subseteq B$.

1.24 We must first show that $A \subseteq B$. Let (x, y) be an arbitrary element of A; then $x^2 + 4y^2 < 1$. Since $x^2 \geq 0$ for all $x \in \mathbb{R}$, this implies that $4y^2 < 1$, and hence $y^2 < \frac{1}{4}$. Hence $y < \frac{1}{2}$. Thus $(x, y) \in B$.

To confirm that A is a *proper* subset of B, we must show that there is an element of B that does not lie in A. The point $(1, -1)$, for example, lies in B, since $-1 < \frac{1}{2}$, but does not lie in A, since

$$1^2 + 4(-1)^2 = 5,$$

which is not less than 1. Therefore A is a proper subset of B.

1.25 (a) 1, -1, 2 are the three solutions of $x^3 - 2x^2 - x + 2 = 0$, so $A = B$.

(b) We showed in the solution to Exercise 1.23(c) that $A \subseteq B$.

If $\dfrac{x^2}{4} + \dfrac{y^2}{9} = 1$, then $(x/2, y/3)$ lies on the unit circle, so we can find $t \in [0, 2\pi]$ such that $x/2 = \cos t$ and $y/3 = \sin t$. Hence $x = 2\cos t$ and $y = 3\sin t$, so $B \subseteq A$.

Since $A \subseteq B$ and $B \subseteq A$, it follows that $A = B$.

(c) The set B contains some negative numbers (for example, -1) which cannot be expressed as $\dfrac{p}{q}$ for $p, q \in \mathbb{N}$. Hence $A \neq B$.

1.26 (a) $A \cup B = \{0, 2, 4, 5, 6\}$,
$A \cap B = \{4\}$,
$A - B = \{0, 2\}$.

(b) $A \cup B = (-5, 17]$,
$A \cap B = [2, 3]$,
$A - B = (-5, 2)$.

(c) $A \cup B = B$,
$A \cap B = A$,
$A - B = \emptyset$.

2.1 (a) This is a translation of the plane that moves each point to the right by 2 units and up by 3 units.

(b) This is a reflection of the plane in the x-axis.

(c) This is a rotation of the plane through $\pi/2$ anticlockwise about the origin.

2.2 Only diagram (b) corresponds to a function.

Diagram (a) does not correspond to a function, as there is no arrow from the element 3.

Diagram (c) does not correspond to a function, as there are two arrows from the element 1.

2.3 The images of the elements of A are
$$f(0) = 9, \ f(1) = 8, \ f(2) = 7, \ f(3) = 6, \ f(4) = 5,$$
$$f(5) = 4, \ f(6) = 3, \ f(7) = 2, \ f(8) = 1, \ f(9) = 0.$$
So the image of f is $\{0, 1, 2, 3, 4, 5, 6, 7, 8, 9\} = A$.

2.4 Only diagram (a) corresponds to an onto function.

Diagram (b) does not even correspond to a function, as there is no arrow from the element 4.

Diagram (c) corresponds to a function that is not onto, as there is no arrow going to the element 1.

2.5 (a) The sketch of the graph of f below suggests that $f(\mathbb{R}) = [1, \infty)$.

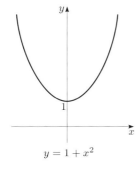

$$y = 1 + x^2$$

Let $x \in \mathbb{R}$; then $f(x) = 1 + x^2$. Since $x^2 \geq 0$, we have $1 + x^2 \geq 1$ and so $f(\mathbb{R}) \subseteq [1, \infty)$.

We must show that $f(\mathbb{R}) \supseteq [1, \infty)$.

Let $y \in [1, \infty)$. We must show that there exists $x \in \mathbb{R}$ such that $f(x) = y$; that is, $1 + x^2 = y$.

Now $x = \sqrt{y - 1}$ is real, since $y \geq 1$, and satisfies $f(x) = y$, as required. (Alternatively, $x = -\sqrt{y - 1}$ is real and satisfies $f(x) = y$.)

Thus $f(\mathbb{R}) \supseteq [1, \infty)$.

Since $f(\mathbb{R}) \subseteq [1, \infty)$ and $f(\mathbb{R}) \supseteq [1, \infty)$, it follows that $f(\mathbb{R}) = [1, \infty)$, so the image of f is $[1, \infty)$, as expected.

The interval $[1, \infty)$ is not the whole of the codomain $\mathbb{R}$, so f is not onto.

(b) This function is a reflection of the plane in the x-axis. This suggests that $f(\mathbb{R}^2) = \mathbb{R}^2$. We know that $f(\mathbb{R}^2) \subseteq \mathbb{R}^2$, so we must show that $f(\mathbb{R}^2) \supseteq \mathbb{R}^2$.

Let $(x', y') \in \mathbb{R}^2$. We must show that there exists $(x, y) \in \mathbb{R}^2$ such that $f(x, y) = (x', y')$; that is,
$$x' = x, \quad y' = -y.$$
Rearranging these equations, we obtain
$$x = x', \quad y = -y'.$$
Let $(x, y) = (x', -y')$; then $(x, y) \in \mathbb{R}^2$ and $f(x, y) = (x', y')$, as required.

Thus $f(\mathbb{R}^2) \supseteq \mathbb{R}^2$.

Since $f(\mathbb{R}^2) \subseteq \mathbb{R}^2$ and $f(\mathbb{R}^2) \supseteq \mathbb{R}^2$, it follows that $f(\mathbb{R}^2) = \mathbb{R}^2$, so the image of f is $\mathbb{R}^2$, as expected.

The codomain of f is also $\mathbb{R}^2$, so f is onto.

2.6 Only diagram (c) corresponds to a one-one function.

Diagram (a) corresponds to a function that is not one-one, as there are two arrows going to the element 3.

Diagram (b) does not even correspond to a function, as there is no arrow from the element 2.

2.7 (a) This function is not one-one since, for example,
$$f(2) = f(-2) = 1 + 4 = 5.$$

(b) This function is a reflection of the plane in the x-axis, so we expect it to be one-one. We now prove this algebraically.

Suppose that $f(x_1, y_1) = f(x_2, y_2)$; then
$$(x_1, -y_1) = (x_2, -y_2).$$
Thus
$$x_1 = x_2 \quad \text{and} \quad -y_1 = -y_2.$$
So
$$y_1 = y_2.$$
Hence $(x_1, y_1) = (x_2, y_2)$, so f is one-one.

2.8 (a) In Exercise 2.7 we saw that f is not one-one, so f does not have an inverse function.

(b) In Exercise 2.7 we saw that f is one-one, so f has an inverse function.

In Exercise 2.5 we saw that the image of f is $\mathbb{R}^2$ and, for each $(x', y') \in \mathbb{R}^2$, we have

$$(x', y') = f(x', -y').$$

So f^{-1} is the function

$$f^{-1} : \mathbb{R}^2 \longrightarrow \mathbb{R}^2$$
$$(x', y') \longmapsto (x', -y').$$

This can be expressed in terms of x and y as

$$f^{-1} : \mathbb{R}^2 \longrightarrow \mathbb{R}^2$$
$$(x, y) \longmapsto (x, -y).$$

(In this case, f^{-1} is actually equal to f.)

(c) This is a linear function, which suggests that it is one-one. First we confirm this algebraically. Suppose that $f(x_1) = f(x_2)$; then

$$8x_1 + 3 = 8x_2 + 3,$$

so $8x_1 = 8x_2$, and hence $x_1 = x_2$. Thus f is one-one, and so it has an inverse function. We now find the image of f. We suspect that its image is $\mathbb{R}$, so we now prove this algebraically. Let y be an arbitrary element in $\mathbb{R}$. We must show that there exists an element x in the domain $\mathbb{R}$ such that

$$f(x) = y; \quad \text{that is,} \quad 8x + 3 = y.$$

Rearranging this equation, we obtain

$$x = \frac{y - 3}{8}.$$

This is in $\mathbb{R}$ and satisfies $f(x) = y$, as required. Thus the image of f is $\mathbb{R}$.

Hence f^{-1} is the function

$$f^{-1} : \mathbb{R} \longrightarrow \mathbb{R}$$
$$y \longmapsto \frac{y - 3}{8}.$$

This can be expressed in terms of x as

$$f^{-1} : \mathbb{R} \longrightarrow \mathbb{R}$$
$$x \longmapsto \frac{x - 3}{8}.$$

2.9 (a) The function

$$g : [0, \infty) \longrightarrow \mathbb{R}$$
$$x \longmapsto |x|$$

is a restriction of f that is one-one.

(There are many other possibilities.)

2.10 (a) The rule of $g \circ f$ is

$$(g \circ f)(x) = g(f(x)) = g(-x)$$
$$= 3(-x) + 1$$
$$= -3x + 1.$$

Thus $g \circ f$ is the function

$$g \circ f : \mathbb{R} \longrightarrow \mathbb{R}$$
$$x \longmapsto -3x + 1.$$

(b) The rule of $f \circ g$ is

$$(f \circ g)(x) = f(g(x)) = f(3x + 1)$$
$$= -(3x + 1)$$
$$= -3x - 1.$$

Thus $f \circ g$ is the function

$$f \circ g : \mathbb{R} \longrightarrow \mathbb{R}$$
$$x \longmapsto -3x - 1.$$

2.11 The rule of $f \circ g$ is

$$(f \circ g)(x, y) = f(g(x, y)) = f(-x, y)$$
$$= (-x, -y).$$

Thus $f \circ g$ is the function

$$f \circ g : \mathbb{R}^2 \longrightarrow \mathbb{R}^2$$
$$(x, y) \longmapsto (-x, -y).$$

(In this case, $f \circ g = g \circ f$.)

2.12 The rule of $g \circ f$ is

$$(g \circ f)(x) = g(f(x)) = g(3x + 1)$$
$$= \frac{3}{(3x + 1) + 2}$$
$$= \frac{1}{x + 1}.$$

The domain of $g \circ f$ is

$$\{x \in [-1, 1] : f(x) \in \mathbb{R} - \{-2\}\}.$$

If $x \in [-1, 1]$, then $f(x) \in \mathbb{R} - \{-2\}$ unless $f(x) = -2$. Now $f(x) = -2$ when

$$3x + 1 = -2,$$

that is, when

$$x = -1.$$

So the domain of $g \circ f$ is

$$[-1, 1] - \{-1\} = (-1, 1].$$

Thus $g \circ f$ is the function

$$g \circ f : (-1, 1] \longrightarrow \mathbb{R}$$
$$x \longmapsto \frac{1}{x + 1}.$$

2.13 For each $x \in \mathbb{R}$, we have
$$f(g(x)) = f(x-3)$$
$$= (x-3)+3$$
$$= x;$$
that is, $f \circ g = i_{\mathbb{R}}$.

For each $x \in \mathbb{R}$, we have
$$g(f(x)) = g(x+3)$$
$$= (x+3)-3$$
$$= x;$$
that is, $g \circ f = i_{\mathbb{R}}$.

Since $g \circ f = i_{\mathbb{R}}$ and $f \circ g = i_{\mathbb{R}}$, it follows that g is the inverse function of f.

2.14 (a) This function is a *rotation* of the plane through $3\pi/2$ anticlockwise about the origin.

(b) This function is a *translation* of the plane that moves each point to the left by 2 units and up by 1 unit.

2.15 (a)

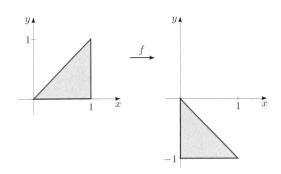

(b)

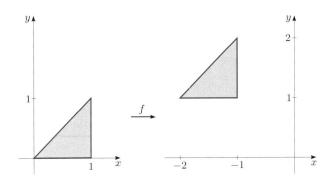

2.16 (a) This function is a rotation (see Exercise 2.1(c)) so we expect to find that $f(\mathbb{R}^2) = \mathbb{R}^2$.

Let $(x, y) \in \mathbb{R}^2$; then $f(x, y) = (-y, x) \in \mathbb{R}^2$, so $f(\mathbb{R}^2) \subseteq \mathbb{R}^2$.

We must now show that $f(\mathbb{R}^2) \supseteq \mathbb{R}^2$.

Let $(x', y') \in \mathbb{R}^2$. We must show that there exists $(x, y) \in \mathbb{R}^2$ such that $f(x, y) = (x', y')$, that is,
$$x' = -y \quad \text{and} \quad y' = x.$$

Rearranging these equations, we obtain
$$x = y' \quad \text{and} \quad y = -x'.$$
So, for each $(x', y') \in \mathbb{R}^2$, we have
$$(x', y') = f(y', -x'),$$
thus $f(\mathbb{R}^2) \supseteq \mathbb{R}^2$.

Since $f(\mathbb{R}^2) \subseteq \mathbb{R}^2$ and $f(\mathbb{R}^2) \supseteq \mathbb{R}^2$, it follows that $f(\mathbb{R}^2) = \mathbb{R}^2$, so f is onto.

(b)

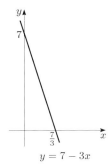

$$y = 7 - 3x$$

The graph above suggests that $f(\mathbb{R}) = \mathbb{R}$. We now prove this algebraically.

Let $x \in \mathbb{R}$; then $7 - 3x \in \mathbb{R}$, so $f(\mathbb{R}) \subseteq \mathbb{R}$.

Let $y \in \mathbb{R}$; then we want to find $x \in \mathbb{R}$ such that $y = 7 - 3x$.

This gives $x = \dfrac{7-y}{3}$, which is in $\mathbb{R}$, so for each $y \in \mathbb{R}$ we have $y = f\left(\dfrac{7-y}{3}\right)$. So $f(\mathbb{R}) \supseteq \mathbb{R}$.

Since $f(\mathbb{R}) \subseteq \mathbb{R}$ and $f(\mathbb{R}) \supseteq \mathbb{R}$, it follows that $f(\mathbb{R}) = \mathbb{R}$, so f is onto.

(c)

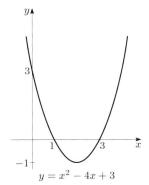

$$y = x^2 - 4x + 3$$

The graph above suggests that $f(\mathbb{R}) = [-1, \infty)$. We now prove this algebraically.

Let $x \in \mathbb{R}$; then
$$f(x) = x^2 - 4x + 3$$
$$= (x-2)^2 - 1 \geq -1.$$
So $f(\mathbb{R}) \subseteq [-1, \infty)$.

Let $y \in [-1, \infty)$. We must show that there exists $x \in \mathbb{R}$ such that $f(x) = y$, that is,
$$x^2 - 4x + 3 = y.$$

This means that
$$(x-2)^2 = y + 1,$$
and we can take $x = 2 + \sqrt{y+1}$, which is in $\mathbb{R}$ since $y + 1 \geq 0$.

So, for each $y \in [-1, \infty)$, we have $y = f(2 + \sqrt{y+1})$.
Hence $f(\mathbb{R}) \supseteq [-1, \infty)$.

Since $f(\mathbb{R}) \subseteq [-1, \infty)$ and $f(\mathbb{R}) \supseteq [-1, \infty)$, it follows that $f(\mathbb{R}) = [-1, \infty)$.

Since $f(\mathbb{R}) \neq \mathbb{R}$, f is not onto.

(d)

$$y = 2x + 3$$

The graph above suggests that $f([0, 1]) = [3, 5]$. We now prove this algebraically.

Let $x \in [0, 1]$. Then $0 \le x \le 1$, so $0 \le 2x \le 2$, so $3 \le 2x + 3 \le 5$. Hence $f(x) \in [3, 5]$. Thus $f([0, 1]) \subseteq [3, 5]$.

Let $y \in [3, 5]$; then we want to find $x \in [0, 1]$ such that $y = 2x + 3$. This gives $x = \dfrac{y - 3}{2}$. Now $3 \le y \le 5$, so $0 \le y - 3 \le 2$, so $0 \le \dfrac{y - 3}{2} \le 1$. Thus $\dfrac{y - 3}{2} \in [0, 1]$, as required. So for each $y \in [3, 5]$ we have $y = f\left(\dfrac{y - 3}{2}\right)$, where $\dfrac{y - 3}{2} \in [0, 1]$. So $f([0, 1]) \supseteq [3, 5]$.

Since $f([0, 1]) \subseteq [3, 5]$ and $f([0, 1]) \supseteq [3, 5]$, it follows that $f([0, 1]) = [3, 5]$. So f is not onto.

2.17 (a) This function f is a rotation of the plane, so we expect f to be one-one. We now prove this algebraically.

Suppose that $f(x_1, y_1) = f(x_2, y_2)$; then
$$(-y_1, x_1) = (-y_2, x_2),$$
so
$$-y_1 = -y_2 \quad \text{and} \quad x_1 = x_2.$$
Thus $(x_1, y_1) = (x_2, y_2)$, so f is one-one.

(b) The graph in the solution to Exercise 2.16(b) suggests that f is one-one. We prove this algebraically.

Suppose that $f(x_1) = f(x_2)$; then
$$7 - 3x_1 = 7 - 3x_2.$$
Thus $x_1 = x_2$, so f is one-one.

(c) The graph in the solution to Exercise 2.16(c) suggests that f is not one-one. To show that this is so, we find two points in the domain of f with the same image. For example,
$$f(0) = f(4) = 3,$$
so f is not one-one.

(d) The graph in the solution to Exercise 2.16(d) suggests that f is one-one. We prove this algebraically.

Suppose that $f(x_1) = f(x_2)$; then
$$2x_1 + 3 = 2x_2 + 3.$$
Thus $x_1 = x_2$, so f is one-one.

2.18 (a) We have shown in Exercise 2.17(a) that f is one-one, so f has an inverse, and we have shown in the solution to Exercise 2.16(a) that
$$(x', y') = f(y', -x'),$$
so the inverse of f is the function
$$f^{-1} : \mathbb{R}^2 \longrightarrow \mathbb{R}^2$$
$$(x', y') \longmapsto (y', -x').$$
This can be expressed in terms of x and y as
$$f^{-1} : \mathbb{R}^2 \longrightarrow \mathbb{R}^2$$
$$(x, y) \longmapsto (y, -x).$$

(b) We have shown in the solutions to Exercises 2.16(b) and 2.17(b) that f is one-one and that
$$y = f\left(\frac{7 - y}{3}\right), \quad \text{for } y \in \mathbb{R}.$$
Hence f has an inverse
$$f^{-1} : \mathbb{R} \longrightarrow \mathbb{R}$$
$$y \longmapsto \frac{7 - y}{3}.$$
This can be expressed in terms of x as
$$f^{-1} : \mathbb{R} \longrightarrow \mathbb{R}$$
$$x \longmapsto \frac{7 - x}{3}.$$

(c) We have shown in Exercise 2.17(c) that f is not one-one, so f does not have an inverse.

(d) We have shown in the solutions to Exercises 2.16(d) and 2.17(d) that f is one-one and that the image of f is $[3, 5]$. We also showed that
$$y = f\left(\frac{y - 3}{2}\right), \quad \text{for } y \in [3, 5].$$
Hence f has an inverse
$$f^{-1} : [3, 5] \longrightarrow [0, 1]$$
$$y \longmapsto \frac{y - 3}{2}.$$
This can be expressed in terms of x as
$$f^{-1} : [3, 5] \longrightarrow [0, 1]$$
$$x \longmapsto \frac{x - 3}{2}.$$

2.19 (a) Since any number in the domain of g has an image under g which is in $\mathbb{R}$, and hence in the domain of f, the domain of $f \circ g$ is the domain of g.

Also,
$$(f \circ g)(x) = f\left(\frac{1}{x^2 - 4}\right) = 7 - 3\left(\frac{1}{x^2 - 4}\right).$$
Hence the composite is the function
$$f \circ g : \mathbb{R} - \{2, -2\} \longrightarrow \mathbb{R}$$
$$x \longmapsto 7 - \frac{3}{x^2 - 4}.$$

(b) Since any point in the domain of g has an image under g which is in $\mathbb{R}^2$, and hence in the domain of f, the domain of $f \circ g$ is the domain of g.

Also,
$$(f \circ g)(x, y) = f(y, x) = (-x, y).$$
Hence the composite is the function
$$f \circ g : \mathbb{R}^2 \longrightarrow \mathbb{R}^2$$
$$(x, y) \longmapsto (-x, y).$$

3.1 (a) The negation can be expressed as '$x = \frac{3}{5}$ is not a solution of the equation $3x + 5 = 0$'.

(b) The negation can be expressed as 'π is greater than or equal to 5'.

(c) The negation can be expressed as 'there is no integer that is divisible by 3 but not by 6', or, alternatively, 'every integer that is divisible by 3 is also divisible by 6'.

(d) The negation can be expressed as 'there is a real number x that does not satisfy the inequality $x^2 \geq 0$'.

(e) The negation can be expressed as 'at least one of the integers m and n is even'.

(f) The negation can be expressed as 'the integers m and n are both even'.

3.2 (a) The statement can be rewritten as 'if $x^2 - 2x + 1 = 0$, then $(x - 1)^2 = 0$'. This is true.

(b) The statement can be rewritten as 'if n is odd, then n^3 is odd'. This is true.

(c) The statement can be rewritten as 'if a given integer is divisible by 3, then it is also divisible by 6'. This is false.

(d) The statement can be rewritten as 'if $x > 2$, then $x > 4$'. This is false.

3.3 (a) The converse is 'if $m + n$ is even, then m and n are both odd'. The given statement is true, and its converse is false.

(b) The converse is 'if $m + n$ is odd, then one of the pair m, n is even and the other is odd'. The given statement and its converse are both true.

3.4 (a) The two implications are 'if the product mn is odd, then both m and n are odd', and 'if both m and n are odd, then the product mn is odd'. Both implications are true, so the equivalence is true.

(b) The two implications are 'if the product mn is even, then both m and n are even', and 'if both m and n are even, then the product mn is even'. The first implication is false, and the second is true. The equivalence is false.

3.5 (a) Suppose that n is an even integer. Then $n = 2k$, where $k \in \mathbb{Z}$, so
$$n^2 = (2k)^2 = 4k^2 = 2(2k^2).$$
Hence n^2 is even, as required.

(b) Let m and n be multiples of k. Then $m = ka$ and $n = kb$, where a and b are integers. Hence
$$m + n = ka + kb = k(a + b).$$
Since $a + b$ is an integer, we deduce that $m + n$ is a multiple of k, as required.

(c) Suppose that one of the pair m, n is even and the other is odd. Then one of them is equal to $2k$ and the other to $2l + 1$, for some integers k and l. Then
$$m + n = 2k + (2l + 1) = 2(k + l) + 1,$$
which shows that $m + n$ is odd.

(d) Let n be a positive integer. We note that
$$n^2 + n = n(n + 1).$$
Either n or $n + 1$ must be even, so $n^2 + n$ is even, as required.

(Alternatively, the implication can be proved by considering two separate cases: the case where n is even, and the case where n is odd. However the above proof is shorter and simpler.)

3.6 (a) Taking $m = 1$ and $n = 3$ provides a counter-example, since then $m + n = 4$, which is even.

(b) The number -3 is a counter-example, because $-3 < 2$ but $((-3)^2 - 2)^2 - (9 - 2)^2 = 7^2 = 49$, which is not less than 4.

(c) We look for a counter-example. Here is a table for the first few values of n.

n	1	2	3
$4^n + 1$	5	17	65

Since $4^3 + 1 = 65$ is not a prime number, it provides a counter-example, so this implication is false.

3.7 (a) Let $P(n)$ be the statement
$$1 + 2 + \cdots + n = \tfrac{1}{2}n(n + 1).$$
Then $P(1)$ is true, since $1 = \tfrac{1}{2}1(1 + 1)$.

Let $k \geq 1$, and assume that $P(k)$ is true:
$$1 + 2 + \cdots + k = \tfrac{1}{2}k(k + 1).$$

We wish to deduce that $P(k+1)$ is true:

$1 + 2 + \cdots + k + (k+1) = \frac{1}{2}(k+1)(k+2)$.

Now

$1 + 2 + \cdots + k + (k+1)$
$= \frac{1}{2}k(k+1) + (k+1)$ (by $P(k)$)
$= (k+1)(\frac{1}{2}k + 1)$
$= \frac{1}{2}(k+1)(k+2)$.

Thus, for $k = 1, 2, \ldots,$

$P(k) \Rightarrow P(k+1)$.

Hence, by mathematical induction, $P(n)$ is true for $n = 1, 2, \ldots$.

(b) Let $P(n)$ be the statement

$1^3 + 2^3 + \cdots + n^3 = \frac{1}{4}n^2(n+1)^2$.

Then $P(1)$ is true, since

$1^3 = 1$ and $\frac{1}{4}1^2(1+1)^2 = 1$.

Let $k \geq 1$, and assume that $P(k)$ is true:

$1^3 + 2^3 + \cdots + k^3 = \frac{1}{4}k^2(k+1)^2$.

We wish to deduce that $P(k+1)$ is true:

$1^3 + 2^3 + \cdots + k^3 + (k+1)^3 = \frac{1}{4}(k+1)^2(k+2)^2$.

Now

$1^3 + 2^3 + \cdots + k^3 + (k+1)^3$
$= \frac{1}{4}k^2(k+1)^2 + (k+1)^3$ (by $P(k)$)
$= (k+1)^2(\frac{1}{4}k^2 + (k+1))$
$= \frac{1}{4}(k+1)^2(k^2 + 4k + 4)$
$= \frac{1}{4}(k+1)^2(k+2)^2$.

Thus, for $k = 1, 2, \ldots,$

$P(k) \Rightarrow P(k+1)$.

Hence, by mathematical induction, $P(n)$ is true for $n = 1, 2, \ldots$.

3.8 (a) Let $P(n)$ be the statement '$4^{2n-3} + 1$ is a multiple of 5'.

Then $P(2)$ is true, because $4^{2 \times 2 - 3} + 1 = 4^1 + 1 = 5$.

Now let $k \geq 2$, and assume that $P(k)$ is true; that is,

$4^{2k-3} + 1$ is a multiple of 5.

We wish to deduce that $P(k+1)$ is true; that is,

$4^{2(k+1)-3} + 1 = 4^{2k-1} + 1$ is a multiple of 5.

Now

$4^{2k-1} + 1 = 4^2 4^{2k-3} + 1$
$= 16 \times 4^{2k-3} + 1$
$= 15 \times 4^{2k-3} + 4^{2k-3} + 1$.

The first term here is a multiple of 5, and $4^{2k-3} + 1$ is a multiple of 5, by $P(k)$. Therefore $4^{2k-1} + 1$ is a multiple of 5. Hence

$P(k) \Rightarrow P(k+1)$, for $k = 2, 3, \ldots$.

Hence, by mathematical induction, $P(n)$ is true, for $n = 2, 3, \ldots$.

(b) Let $P(n)$ be the statement $5^n < n!$.

Then $P(12)$ is true, because $5^{12} = 2.44 \times 10^8$ and $12! = 4.79 \times 10^8$, both to three significant figures.

Now let $k \geq 12$, and assume that $P(k)$ is true; that is,

$5^k < k!$.

We wish to deduce that $P(k+1)$ is true; that is,

$5^{(k+1)} < (k+1)!$.

Now

$5^{k+1} = 5 \times 5^k$
$< 5 \times k!$ (by $P(k)$)
$< (k+1)k!$
$= (k+1)!$,

where we have used the fact that $k \geq 12$, so $k + 1 \geq 13 > 5$. Hence

$P(k) \Rightarrow P(k+1)$, for $k = 12, 13, \ldots$.

Hence, by mathematical induction, $P(n)$ is true, for $n = 12, 13, \ldots$.

3.9 (a) Suppose that there exist real numbers a and b with $ab > \frac{1}{2}(a^2 + b^2)$. Then $a^2 - 2ab + b^2 < 0$; that is, $(a - b)^2 < 0$. This is a contradiction, so our supposition must be false. Hence there are no such real numbers a and b.

(b) Suppose that there exist integers m and n with $5m + 15n = 357$. The left-hand side of this equation is a multiple of 5, so the right-hand side is also. But this is a contradiction, so our supposition must be false. Hence there are no such integers m and n.

3.10 Suppose that $n = a + 2b$, where a and b are positive real numbers. Suppose also that $a < \frac{1}{2}n$ and $b < \frac{1}{4}n$. Then

$n = a + 2b < \frac{1}{2}n + 2(\frac{1}{4}n) = n$.

This contradiction shows that the supposition that $a < \frac{1}{2}n$ and $b < \frac{1}{4}n$ must be false; that is we must have $a \geq \frac{1}{2}n$ or $b \geq \frac{1}{4}n$.

3.11 (a) We prove the contrapositive implication, which is

n is odd $\Rightarrow n^3$ is odd.

Suppose that n is odd. Then $n = 2k + 1$ for some integer k. Then

$n^3 = (2k+1)^3$
$= (2k+1)(4k^2 + 4k + 1)$
$= 8k^3 + 12k^2 + 6k + 1$
$= 2(4k^3 + 6k^2 + 3k) + 1$,

which is odd.

(b) We prove the contrapositive implication, which is 'if at least one of m and n is even, then mn is even'.

Suppose that at least one of m and n is even; without loss of generality, we can take it to be m (since otherwise we can just interchange m and n). Then $m = 2k$ for some integer k. Hence $mn = 2kn$, which is even.

(c) Let n be an integer which is greater than 1. We prove the contrapositive implication, which is 'if n is not a prime number, then n is divisible by at least one of the primes less than or equal to $\sqrt{n}$'.

Suppose that n is not a prime number. Then $n = ab$ for some integers a, b, where $1 < a, b < n$. By the result of Example 3.15, at least one of a and b is less than or equal to $\sqrt{n}$. This number has a prime factor, which must also be less than or equal to $\sqrt{n}$, and this prime factor must also be a factor of n. This proves the required contrapositive implication.

3.12 (a), (b) and (c) all have the same meaning.

(d) and (f) have the same meaning.

(You may like to show that (a) is true, and hence that (b) and (c) are true; that (d) and (f) are true, but (e) is false.)

3.13 $13^2 = 169$ and $17^2 = 289$, so we need check only the primes 2, 3, 5, 7, 11, 13.

221 is divisible by 13 ($221 = 13 \times 17$), so it is not prime.

223 is not divisible by any of 2, 3, 5, 7, 11 and 13, so it is prime.

3.14 **(a)** This statement is true.

We have
$$n^3 - n = n(n^2 - 1) = n(n-1)(n+1).$$
Either n is even or $n + 1$ is even, so $n^3 - n$ is even.

(b) This statement is false.

For example, $6 + 4$ is a multiple of 5, but 6 and 4 are not multiples of 5.

(c) This statement is false.

For example, if $\theta = \pi/2$, then
$$\sin 2\theta = \sin \pi = 0,$$
but
$$2 \sin \theta = 2 \sin(\pi/2) = 2.$$

(d) This statement is false.

For example, $f(0) = f(2) = 1$.

(e) This statement is true.

We show that $f \circ g$ is the identity on $\mathbb{R} - \{0\}$ and that $g \circ f$ is the identity on $\mathbb{R} - \{1\}$.

We have
$$(f \circ g)(x) = f\left(1 + \frac{1}{x}\right) = \frac{1}{\left(1 + \dfrac{1}{x}\right) - 1} = x$$
and
$$f \circ g : \mathbb{R} - \{0\} \longrightarrow \mathbb{R} - \{0\}.$$
Also,
$$(g \circ f)(x) = g\left(\frac{1}{x - 1}\right) = 1 + \frac{1}{1/(x-1)}$$
$$= 1 + x - 1 = x$$
and
$$g \circ f : \mathbb{R} - \{1\} \longrightarrow \mathbb{R} - \{1\}.$$
Hence, from Strategy 2.1, g is the inverse of f.

3.15 **(a)** The converse is as follows.

If $m - n$ is an even integer, then m and n are both even integers.

(b) The original statement is true.

Suppose that m and n are both even; then
$$m = 2p, \quad n = 2q, \quad \text{where } p, q \text{ are integers.}$$
Then
$$m - n = 2p - 2q$$
$$= 2(p - q),$$
which is even.

The converse is false.

For example,
$$7 - 3 = 4 \text{ is even,}$$
but 7 and 3 are both odd.

3.16 **(a)** Let $P(n)$ be the statement
$$\frac{1}{1 \times 2} + \frac{1}{2 \times 3} + \cdots + \frac{1}{(n-1)n} = \frac{n-1}{n}.$$
Then $P(2)$ is true, since
$$\frac{1}{1 \times 2} = \frac{1}{2} = \frac{2-1}{2}.$$
Assume that $P(k)$ is true:
$$\frac{1}{1 \times 2} + \frac{1}{2 \times 3} + \cdots + \frac{1}{(k-1)k} = \frac{k-1}{k}.$$
We wish to deduce that $P(k+1)$ is true:
$$\frac{1}{1 \times 2} + \frac{1}{2 \times 3} + \cdots + \frac{1}{(k-1)k} + \frac{1}{k(k+1)}$$
$$= \frac{k}{k+1}.$$
Now
$$\frac{1}{1 \times 2} + \frac{1}{2 \times 3} + \cdots + \frac{1}{(k-1)k} + \frac{1}{k(k+1)}$$
$$= \frac{k-1}{k} + \frac{1}{k(k+1)} \quad \text{(by } P(k)\text{)}$$
$$= \frac{(k-1)(k+1) + 1}{k(k+1)}$$
$$= \frac{k^2}{k(k+1)} = \frac{k}{k+1}.$$

Thus, for $k = 2, 3, \ldots,$

$P(k) \Rightarrow P(k+1).$

Hence, by mathematical induction, $P(n)$ is true for $n = 2, 3, \ldots.$

(b) Let $P(n)$ be the statement

$3^{2n} - 1$ is divisible by 8.

Then $P(1)$ is true, since

$3^2 - 1 = 9 - 1 = 8,$

which is divisible by 8.

Assume that $P(k)$ is true:

$3^{2k} - 1$ is divisible by 8.

We wish to deduce that $P(k+1)$ is true:

$3^{2(k+1)} - 1$ is divisible by 8.

Now

$$3^{2(k+1)} - 1 = 3^2 3^{2k} - 1$$
$$= 9 \times 3^{2k} - 1$$
$$= 8 \times 3^{2k} + (3^{2k} - 1),$$

which is also divisible by 8, since $P(k)$ is true.

Thus, for $k = 1, 2, \ldots,$

$P(k) \Rightarrow P(k+1).$

Hence, by mathematical induction, $P(n)$ is true for $n = 1, 2, \ldots.$

3.17 Suppose that the given statement is false; that is, there are real numbers a and b for which

$(a+b)^2 < 4ab.$

Then

$a^2 + 2ab + b^2 < 4ab,$

so

$a^2 - 2ab + b^2 < 0,$

so

$(a-b)^2 < 0.$

But $(a-b)^2$ is a square, so cannot be negative. This is a contradiction, so the given statement must be true.

Hence

$(a+b)^2 \geq 4ab$ for all real numbers a and $b.$

3.18 (a) The contrapositive is as follows.

If n is not divisible by 3,

then n^2 is not divisible by 3.

(b) Suppose that n is not divisible by 3. Then

$n = 3k + 1$ or $n = 3k + 2,$

for some integer $k.$

If $n = 3k + 1,$ then

$$n^2 = 9k^2 + 6k + 1$$
$$= 3k(3k + 2) + 1,$$

which is not divisible by 3.

If $n = 3k + 2,$ then

$$n^2 = 9k^2 + 12k + 4$$
$$= 3(3k^2 + 4k + 1) + 1,$$

which is not divisible by 3.

Hence the contrapositive is true.
Hence the original statement is true.

3.19 (a) This statement is false.

For example, $-4 < 3,$ but $(-4)^2 \not< 3^2.$

(b) This statement is false.

For example, if $x = 1,$ then $x^2 - x = 0,$ not 2.

(c) This statement is true.

One value of x satisfying $x^2 - x = 2$ is $x = 2.$

(d) This statement is false.

$$x^2 - x = -1 \Leftrightarrow x^2 - x + 1 = 0$$
$$\Leftrightarrow \left(x - \tfrac{1}{2}\right)^2 + \tfrac{3}{4} = 0,$$

which is not possible for any real $x.$

(e) This statement is false.

For example, if $x = y = 1,$ then x/y and y/x are both the integer 1.

(f) This statement is true.

We prove it by mathematical induction.

Let $P(n)$ be the statement

$1^2 + 2^2 + \cdots + n^2 = \tfrac{1}{6}n(n+1)(2n+1).$

Then $P(1)$ is true, since

$$\tfrac{1}{6} \times 1 \times (1+1)(2+1) = \frac{2 \times 3}{6} = 1 = 1^2.$$

Assume that $P(k)$ is true:

$1^2 + 2^2 + \cdots + k^2 = \tfrac{1}{6}k(k+1)(2k+1).$

We wish to deduce that $P(k+1)$ is true:

$$1^2 + 2^2 + \cdots + (k+1)^2$$
$$= \tfrac{1}{6}(k+1)(k+2)(2k+3).$$

Now,

$$1^2 + 2^2 + \cdots + k^2 + (k+1)^2$$
$$= \tfrac{1}{6}k(k+1)(2k+1) + (k+1)^2 \quad \text{(by } P(k)\text{)}$$
$$= \tfrac{1}{6}(k+1)(k(2k+1) + 6(k+1))$$
$$= \tfrac{1}{6}(k+1)(2k^2 + 7k + 6)$$
$$= \tfrac{1}{6}(k+1)(k+2)(2k+3).$$

Hence

$P(k) \Rightarrow P(k+1),$ for $k \geq 1.$

Hence, by mathematical induction, $P(n)$ is true for $n = 1, 2, \ldots.$

(g) Let $P(n)$ be the statement
$$\left(1 - \frac{1}{2}\right)\left(1 - \frac{1}{3}\right)\cdots\left(1 - \frac{1}{n}\right) = \frac{1}{2n}.$$
Then $P(2)$ is false, since
$$1 - \tfrac{1}{2} \neq \tfrac{1}{4}.$$
Hence the statement is false.

(In fact, as you can check,
$$P(k) \text{ is true} \Rightarrow P(k+1) \text{ is true}, \quad \text{for } k \geq 2;$$
that is, step 2 of a proof by mathematical induction works, even though step 1 does not.

The correct expression for the product is $1/n$.)

4.1 (a) By Theorem 4.1, the coefficient of $a^5 b^4$ in $(a + b)^9$ is
$$\binom{9}{4} = \frac{9!}{4!\,5!} = \frac{9 \times 8 \times 7 \times 6}{4 \times 3 \times 2 \times 1} = 126.$$

(b) By Theorem 4.1, the term involving x^4 in $(1 + 2x)^5$ is
$$\binom{5}{4} 1^1 \times (2x)^4 = \frac{5!}{4!\,1!} \times 2^4 x^4$$
$$= (5 \times 16)x^4$$
$$= 80x^4,$$
so the required coefficient is 80.

4.2 (a) By Theorem 4.1, with b replaced by $-b$,
$$(a - b)^n$$
$$= (a + (-b))^n$$
$$= \binom{n}{0} a^n + \binom{n}{1} a^{n-1}(-b) + \cdots$$
$$+ \binom{n}{k} a^{n-k}(-b)^k + \cdots + \binom{n}{n}(-b)^n$$
$$= \binom{n}{0} a^n - \binom{n}{1} a^{n-1}b + \cdots$$
$$+ (-1)^k \binom{n}{k} a^{n-k}b^k + \cdots + (-1)^n \binom{n}{n} b^n.$$

(b) If $a = 1$ and $b = 1$, then $a - b = 0$, so we obtain
$$0 = \binom{n}{0} - \binom{n}{1} + \cdots + (-1)^k \binom{n}{k} + \cdots$$
$$+ (-1)^n \binom{n}{n}.$$
For $n = 4$, this identity is
$$0 = \binom{4}{0} - \binom{4}{1} + \binom{4}{2} - \binom{4}{3} + \binom{4}{4}$$
$$= 1 - 4 + 6 - 4 + 1$$
$$= 0,$$
as expected.

4.3 (a) For $n = 5$, the Geometric Series Identity is
$$a^5 - b^5 = (a - b)(a^4 + a^3b + a^2b^2 + ab^3 + b^4).$$

(b) If n is an odd positive integer, then
$$(-b)^n = (-1)^n b^n = -b^n,$$
so
$$a^n - (-b)^n = a^n + b^n.$$
By Theorem 4.2,
$$a^n - (-b)^n = (a - (-b))(a^{n-1} + a^{n-2}(-b) + \cdots$$
$$+ a(-b)^{n-2} + (-b)^{n-1}),$$
so, since $n - 1$ is even and $n - 2$ is odd,
$$a^n + b^n = (a + b)(a^{n-1} - a^{n-2}b + \cdots$$
$$- ab^{n-2} + b^{n-1}),$$
as required.

For $n = 5$, we have
$$a^5 + b^5 = (a + b)(a^4 - a^3b + a^2b^2 - ab^3 + b^4).$$

4.4 Using the corollary to Theorem 4.2, with $a = 1$ and $r = \frac{1}{2}$, we obtain
$$1 + \frac{1}{2} + \frac{1}{4} + \cdots + \frac{1}{2^{n-1}}$$
$$= 1 + \tfrac{1}{2} + \left(\tfrac{1}{2}\right)^2 + \cdots + \left(\tfrac{1}{2}\right)^{n-1}$$
$$= 1\left(\frac{1 - \left(\tfrac{1}{2}\right)^n}{1 - \tfrac{1}{2}}\right)$$
$$= 2\left(1 - \frac{1}{2^n}\right)$$
$$= 2 - \frac{1}{2^{n-1}}.$$

4.5 By the Polynomial Factorisation Theorem, $x + 3$ is a factor of $p(x)$ if and only if $p(-3) = 0$, that is,
$$0 = (-3)^3 + c(-3)^2 + 6(-3) + 36$$
$$= -27 + 9c - 18 + 36$$
$$= 9c - 9.$$
This equation has just one solution, $c = 1$, so $x + 3$ is a factor of $p(x)$ if and only if $c = 1$.

4.6 (a) (i) Since all the roots are integers, the only possible roots are the factors of 4, that is, $\pm 1, \pm 2, \pm 4$. Considering these in turn, we obtain the following table.

x	1	-1	2	-2	4	-4
$p(x)$	2	0	0	-16	20	-108

So the only solutions are $x = -1$ and $x = 2$. In fact,
$$x^3 - 3x^2 + 4 = (x + 1)(x - 2)(x - 2).$$

(ii) Since all the roots are integers, the only possible roots are the factors of -15, that is, $\pm 1, \pm 3, \pm 5, \pm 15$. Considering these in turn, we obtain the following table.

x	1	-1	3	-3	5	$\cdots$
$p(x)$	0	-48	0	-192	0	$\cdots$

We do not need to work out any more values, as we already have three roots: $x = 1$, $x = 3$ and $x = 5$. So
$$x^3 - 9x^2 + 23x - 15 = (x - 1)(x - 3)(x - 5).$$

(b) A suitable equation is
$$(x - 1)(x - 2)(x - 3)(x + 3) = 0,$$
that is,
$$x^4 - 3x^3 - 7x^2 + 27x - 18 = 0.$$

4.7 (a) $(a + 3b)^4$
$$= \binom{4}{0} a^4 + \binom{4}{1} a^3(3b) + \binom{4}{2} a^2(3b)^2$$
$$\qquad + \binom{4}{3} a(3b)^3 + \binom{4}{4}(3b)^4$$
$$= a^4 + 4a^3 3b + 6a^2 9b^2 + 4a27b^3 + 81b^4$$
$$= a^4 + 12a^3 b + 54a^2 b^2 + 108ab^3 + 81b^4$$

(b) $(1 - t)^7$
$$= \binom{7}{0} + \binom{7}{1}(-t) + \binom{7}{2}(-t)^2$$
$$\qquad + \binom{7}{3}(-t)^3 + \binom{7}{4}(-t)^4 + \binom{7}{5}(-t)^5$$
$$\qquad + \binom{7}{6}(-t)^6 + \binom{7}{7}(-t)^7$$
$$= 1 - 7t + 21t^2 - 35t^3 + 35t^4 - 21t^5 + 7t^6 - t^7$$

4.8 (a) The coefficient of $a^3 b^7$ is
$$\binom{10}{7} = \frac{10 \times 9 \times 8}{3 \times 2} = 120.$$

(b) The coefficient of x^{13} is
$$\binom{15}{13} 2^2 = \frac{15 \times 14}{2} \times 4 = 420.$$

4.9 (a) This is a geometric series with $a = 3$, $r = -\frac{1}{3}$ and $n = 12$ terms, so its sum is
$$3 \frac{\left(1 - \left(-\frac{1}{3}\right)^{12}\right)}{1 - \left(-\frac{1}{3}\right)} = 3 \times \frac{3}{4}\left(1 - \left(\frac{1}{3}\right)^{12}\right)$$
$$= \frac{9}{4}\left(1 - \left(\frac{1}{3}\right)^{12}\right)$$
$$\simeq 2.25.$$

(b) This is a geometric series with first term 1, common ratio $r = \dfrac{a}{b} \neq 1$ and $n + 1$ terms, so its sum is
$$\frac{1 - \left(\frac{a}{b}\right)^{n+1}}{1 - \left(\frac{a}{b}\right)} = \left(\frac{b}{b - a}\right)\left(1 - \left(\frac{a}{b}\right)^{n+1}\right).$$

4.10 (a) Putting $x = 2$, we obtain $16 + 4 - 26 + 6 = 0$, so $x - 2$ is a factor. Hence
$$2x^3 + x^2 - 13x + 6 = (x - 2)(2x^2 + 5x - 3)$$
$$= (x - 2)(x + 3)(2x - 1).$$

(b) Trying integer values which are factors of 10, we find that $x = 1$ is a root, so $x - 1$ is a factor. Hence
$$x^3 + 6x^2 + 3x - 10 = (x - 1)(x^2 + 7x + 10)$$
$$= (x - 1)(x + 2)(x + 5),$$
so the solutions of $x^3 + 6x^2 + 3x - 10 = 0$ are 1, -2 and -5.

(c) $x^2 + x = y^2 + y \iff x^2 - y^2 + x - y = 0$.
We note that $x = y$ is a solution, so $x - y$ is a factor. Hence
$$x^2 - y^2 + x - y = (x - y)(x + y + 1),$$
so $x = y$ or $x = -y - 1$.

4.11 (a) If the sum of the roots is 0 and the product is -30, then the cubic polynomial must be of the form
$$x^3 + cx + 30, \quad \text{for some } c \in \mathbb{R}.$$
If $x = 3$ is a root, then
$$27 + 3c + 30 = 0,$$
so $c = -19$.
Hence the polynomial is $x^3 - 19x + 30$.

(b) We know that $x - 3$ is a factor. Hence
$$x^3 - 19x + 30 = (x - 3)(x^2 + 3x - 10)$$
$$= (x - 3)(x - 2)(x + 5),$$
so the other two roots are 2 and -5.

Index